Virginia End-of-Course Coach

Algebra I

Virginia End-of-Course Coach, Algebra I
229VA
ISBN-13: 978-0-7836-8226-6

Contributing Writer: Theresa Duhon
Cover Image: A cardinal jigsaw puzzle. The cardinal is the state bird of Virginia.
© Steve Byland/Veer; © Axstokes/Dreamstime

Triumph Learning® 136 Madison Avenue, 7th Floor, New York, NY 10016

© 2012 Triumph Learning, LLC
Coach is an imprint of Triumph Learning®

Printed in the United States of America.

10 9 8 7 6 5 4 3 2 1

DEAR STUDENT

Welcome to *Coach*—your learning path to success!

This book provides instruction and practice that will help you master the skills you need to know. It also gives you practice answering the kinds of questions you will see on your state test.

The *Coach* book is organized into chapters and lessons, and includes two Practice tests. Each lesson explains a topic that's important in your study of Math. You can check your understanding of each topic by answering the questions at the end of the lesson and in the chapter reviews. The Practice tests are a model of your state test.

Before you begin the lessons in the book, you can find out how much you already know by taking one of the tests. Then work your way through the lessons. When you finish, take the other test to see how much more you learned!

We wish you lots of success this year, and are glad *Coach* can be a part of it!

Sincerely,

THE COACH TEAM

Table of Contents

Virginia Standards of Learning Correlation Chart

STANDARDS OF LEARNING	ALGEBRA I	COACH Lesson(s)
Expressions and Operations		
STANDARD A.1: The student will represent verbal quantitative situations algebraically and evaluate these expressions for given replacement values of the variables.		7, 8
STANDARD A.2: The student will perform operations on polynomials, including		
A.2.a	applying the laws of exponents to perform operations on expressions;	2
A.2.b	adding, subtracting, multiplying, and dividing polynomials; and	3, 4, 6
A.2.c	factoring completely first- and second-degree binomials and trinomials in one or two variables. Graphing calculators will be used as a tool for factoring and for confirming algebraic factorizations.	5, 21, 22
STANDARD A.3: The student will express the square roots and cube roots of whole numbers and the square root of a monomial algebraic expression in simplest radical form.		1
Equations and Inequalities		
STANDARD A.4: The student will solve multistep linear and quadratic equations in two variables, including		
A.4.a	solving literal equations (formulas) for a given variable;	10
A.4.b	justifying steps used in simplifying expressions and solving equations, using field properties and axioms of equality that are valid for the set of real numbers and its subsets;	9
A.4.c	solving quadratic equations algebraically and graphically;	21, 22
A.4.d	solving multistep linear equations algebraically and graphically;	9, 11
A.4.e	solving systems of two linear equations in two variables algebraically and graphically; and	15, 16
A.4.f	solving real-world problems involving equations and systems of equations. Graphing calculators will be used both as a primary tool in solving problems and to verify algebraic solutions.	17

STANDARDS OF LEARNING	ALGEBRA I	COACH Lesson(s)
	Equations and Inequalities *(continued)*	
STANDARD A.5: The student will solve multistep linear inequalities in two variables, including		
A.5.a	solving multistep linear inequalities algebraically and graphically;	18, 19
A.5.b	justifying steps used in solving inequalities, using axioms of inequality and properties of order that are valid for the set of real numbers and its subsets;	18, 19
A.5.c	solving real-world problems involving inequalities; and	18, 19
A.5.d	solving systems of inequalities.	20
STANDARD A.6: The student will graph linear equations and linear inequalities in two variables, including		
A.6.a	determining the slope of a line when given an equation of the line, the graph of the line, or two points on the line. Slope will be described as rate of change and will be positive, negative, zero, or undefined; and	12, 13, 14, 19
A.6.b	writing the equation of a line when given the graph of the line, two points on the line, or the slope and a point on the line.	13, 14, 19
	Functions	
STANDARD A.7: The student will investigate and analyze function (linear and quadratic) families and their characteristics both algebraically and graphically, including		
A.7.a	determining whether a relation is a function;	23
A.7.b	domain and range;	25
A.7.c	zeros of a function;	26
A.7.d	x- and y-intercepts;	26
A.7.e	finding the values of a function for elements in its domain; and	25
A.7.f	making connections between and among multiple representations of functions including concrete, verbal, numeric, graphic, and algebraic.	13, 17, 21, 23, 24
STANDARD A.8: The student, given a situation in a real-world context, will analyze a relation to determine whether a direct or inverse variation exists, and represent a direct variation algebraically and graphically and an inverse variation algebraically.		27, 28

STANDARDS OF LEARNING	ALGEBRA I	COACH Lesson(s)
	Statistics	
STANDARD A.9: The student, given a set of data, will interpret variation in real-world contexts and calculate and interpret mean absolute deviation, standard deviation, and z-scores.		29, 30, 31, 32
STANDARD A.10: The student will compare and contrast multiple univariate data sets, using box-and-whisker plots.		33
STANDARD A.11: The student will collect and analyze data, determine the equation of the curve of best fit in order to make predictions, and solve real-world problems, using mathematical models. Mathematical models will include linear and quadratic functions.		34, 35

Chapter 1

Expressions and Operations

Square and Cube Roots

SOL: A.3

To **square a number** means to raise it to the power of 2 or to multiply it by itself. For example, 8^2 is read as "eight squared."

$$8^2 = 8 \cdot 8 = 64$$

The opposite, or inverse, of squaring a number is taking its **square root**. The radical symbol, $\sqrt{}$, is used to indicate a square root. The number under that symbol is called the **radicand**.

$\sqrt{64} = 8$, because $8^2 = 64$.

Since $(-8)^2$ is also equal to 64, the number -8 is another square root of 64. The positive number 8 is called the **principal square root** of 64. It is a mathematical convention to consider only the principal, or positive, square root. To indicate the negative square root, write $-\sqrt{64}$.

Any number that has a whole-number square root is a **perfect square**. For example, 64 is a perfect square because $\sqrt{64}$ is equal to a whole number, 8. Below are the first 25 consecutive perfect squares.

1, 4, 9, 16, 25, 36, 49, 64, 81, 100, 121, 144, 169, 196,

225, 256, 289, 324, 361, 400, 441, 484, 529, 576, 625

To take the square root of a perfect square, ask yourself: what whole number multiplied by itself equals that number?

Example 1

What is the value of $\sqrt{225}$?

Strategy   **Decide if the radicand is a perfect square. If so, decide which whole number can be multiplied by itself to get that number.**

Step 1   Decide if the radicand is a perfect square.

Look back at the list of perfect squares.

225 is a perfect square.

Step 2   Ask yourself what whole number multiplied by itself is equal to 225.

If you do not know the answer from memory, use guess and check.

Since the last digit in 225 is 5, 225 is a multiple of 5 but not a multiple of 10.

Guess 25: $25 \cdot 25 = 625 \rightarrow 25$ is too high.

Guess 15: $15 \cdot 15 = 225 \rightarrow 15$ works.

Solution   **The value of $\sqrt{225}$ is 15 because $15^2 = 225$.**

A square root in simplest form is one in which the radicand has no perfect square factors other than 1. The properties below will help you simplify square roots.

Product Property of Square Roots

The square root of a product is equal to the product of the square roots of the factors.

$$\sqrt{ab} = \sqrt{a} \cdot \sqrt{b} \qquad \sqrt{50} = \sqrt{25 \cdot 2} = \sqrt{25} \cdot \sqrt{2} = 5\sqrt{2}$$

Quotient Property of Square Roots

The square root of a quotient is equal to the quotient of the square root of the dividend and the square root of the divisor.

$$\sqrt{\frac{a}{b}} = \frac{\sqrt{a}}{\sqrt{b}} \qquad \sqrt{\frac{9}{16}} = \frac{\sqrt{9}}{\sqrt{16}} = \frac{3}{4}$$

Example 2

Simplify: $\sqrt{72}$

Strategy　　**Use the product property of square roots.**

Step 1　　Find factors of 72 that are perfect squares.

$$72 = 8 \cdot 9 = (2 \cdot 4) \cdot 9$$

Note: 4 and 9 are perfect squares.

Step 2　　Rewrite $\sqrt{72}$ as a product of square roots.

$$\sqrt{72} = \sqrt{2 \cdot 4 \cdot 9} = \sqrt{2} \cdot \sqrt{4} \cdot \sqrt{9}$$

Step 3　　Simplify by taking the square roots of the perfect squares.

$$\sqrt{72} = \sqrt{2} \cdot \sqrt{4} \cdot \sqrt{9}$$
$$\sqrt{72} = \sqrt{2} \cdot 2 \cdot 3$$
$$\sqrt{72} = \sqrt{2} \cdot 6$$
$$\sqrt{72} = 6\sqrt{2}$$

Solution　　$\sqrt{72} = 6\sqrt{2}$

You can also use what you know about square roots to simplify **algebraic expressions**. An algebraic expression is a combination of numbers and variables that are connected by one or more operations. A **variable** is a symbol or letter, such as x, that is used to represent a number.

Example 3

Simplify: $\sqrt{\dfrac{4a^2}{b^2}}$

Strategy   **First simplify the numerator. Then simplify the denominator.**

Step 1   Rewrite the algebraic expression under the square root symbol as the quotient of two square roots.

$$\sqrt{\frac{4a^2}{b^2}} = \frac{\sqrt{4a^2}}{\sqrt{b^2}}$$

Step 2   Rewrite the numerator, $\sqrt{4a^2}$, as the product of two factors.

$$\sqrt{4a^2} = \sqrt{4} \cdot \sqrt{a^2}$$

Step 3   Evaluate each factor in the numerator.

1st factor: $\sqrt{4} = \sqrt{2 \cdot 2} = \sqrt{2^2} = 2$

2nd factor: $\sqrt{a^2} = \sqrt{a \cdot a} = a$

$$\sqrt{4a^2} = \sqrt{4} \cdot \sqrt{a^2} = 2 \cdot a = 2a$$

Step 4   Evaluate the denominator.

$$\sqrt{b^2} = \sqrt{b \cdot b} = b$$

Step 5   Simplify the original expression.

$$\sqrt{\frac{4a^2}{b^2}} = \frac{2a}{b}$$

Solution   **The expression can be simplified as $\dfrac{2a}{b}$.**

To **cube a number** means to raise it to the power of 3.

$$2^3 = 2 \cdot 2 \cdot 2 = 8$$

The inverse of cubing a number is taking its **cube root**. The cube root is denoted by $\sqrt[3]{}$.

A **perfect cube**, such as 8, has a cube root that is an integer.

$$\sqrt[3]{8} = \sqrt[3]{2 \cdot 2 \cdot 2} = 2$$

The product and quotient properties of radicals that apply to square roots also extend to the cube root and the *n*th root of a number.

Although you can take the square root of only positive numbers and zero in the real number system, you can take the cube root of any real number: positive, negative, or zero.

$$\sqrt[3]{-8} = \sqrt[3]{(-2) \cdot (-2) \cdot (-2)} = -2$$

Example 4

Simplify: $\sqrt[3]{64}$

Strategy   **Use the product property of square roots.**

Step 1   Write 64 as a product of its perfect cube factors.

$$\sqrt[3]{64} = \sqrt[3]{8 \cdot 8}$$

Step 2   Apply the property.

$$\sqrt[3]{8 \cdot 8} = \sqrt[3]{8} \cdot \sqrt[3]{8}$$

Step 3   Simplify.

$$\sqrt[3]{8} \cdot \sqrt[3]{8} = 2 \cdot 2 = 4$$

Solution $\sqrt[3]{64} = 4$

A cube root in simplest form is one in which the radicand has no perfect cube factors other than 1.

Example 5

Simplify: $\sqrt[3]{-250}$

Strategy   **Use the product property of radicals.**

Step 1   Find perfect cube factors of 250.

Fully factoring a number will help in identifying perfect cube factors.

$250 = 2 \cdot 125 = 2 \cdot 5 \cdot 25 = 2 \cdot 5 \cdot 5 \cdot 5$

Step 2   Write -250 as a product of cube roots, with the perfect cube as the negative factor.

$$\sqrt[3]{-250} = \sqrt[3]{2 \cdot (-125)} = \sqrt[3]{2} \cdot \sqrt[3]{-125}$$

Step 3   Simplify.

$$\sqrt[3]{2} \cdot \sqrt[3]{(-5)^3} = \sqrt[3]{2} \cdot (-5) = -5\sqrt[3]{2}$$

Solution   **When simplified, $\sqrt[3]{-250} = -5\sqrt[3]{2}$.**

Coached Example

Simplify: $\sqrt{x^3 y^4}$

Rewrite as a product of two square roots.

$\sqrt{x^3 y^4} = \sqrt{x^3} \cdot \sqrt{\underline{\hspace{1cm}}}$

The term x^3 is the product of the perfect square _____ and _____.

Simplify $\sqrt{x^3}$ using the square root of the perfect square factor.

$\sqrt{x^3} = \sqrt{\underline{\hspace{1cm}}} \cdot \sqrt{\underline{\hspace{1cm}}} = \underline{\hspace{1cm}} \cdot \underline{\hspace{1cm}} = \underline{\hspace{1cm}}$

Simplify $\sqrt{y^4}$.

$\sqrt{y^4} = \sqrt{\underline{\hspace{1cm}} \cdot \underline{\hspace{1cm}}} = \sqrt{\underline{\hspace{1cm}}} \cdot \sqrt{\underline{\hspace{1cm}}} = \underline{\hspace{1cm}} \cdot \underline{\hspace{1cm}} = \underline{\hspace{1cm}}$

Simplify the original expression.

$\sqrt{x^3 y^4} = \underline{\hspace{1cm}} \cdot \underline{\hspace{1cm}} = \underline{\hspace{1cm}}$

The simplest form of $\sqrt{x^3 y^4}$ is _____.

Lesson Practice

Choose the correct answer.

1. What is the value of $\sqrt{196}$?

   A. 13

   B. 14

   C. 16

   D. 98

2. What is the value of $\sqrt[3]{\frac{8}{125}}$?

   A. $\frac{2}{25}$

   B. $\frac{4}{25}$

   C. $\frac{2}{5}$

   D. $\frac{4}{5}$

3. Simplify: $\sqrt{98}$

   A. $2\sqrt{7}$

   B. 9

   C. $7\sqrt{2}$

   D. $7\sqrt{7}$

4. Simplify: $\sqrt{9y^5}$

   A. $3y^2\sqrt{y}$

   B. $3y^3$

   C. $3y^4\sqrt{y}$

   D. $3y\sqrt{y^2}$

5. Simplify: $\sqrt[3]{-54}$

   A. $3\sqrt[3]{6}$

   B. $3\sqrt[3]{2}$

   C. $-3\sqrt[3]{2}$

   D. $-3\sqrt[3]{6}$

6. Simplify: $\sqrt{\frac{32}{81}}$

   A. $\frac{16}{9}$

   B. $\frac{2\sqrt{2}}{3}$

   C. $\frac{2\sqrt{2}}{9}$

   D. $\frac{4\sqrt{2}}{9}$

7. Simplify: $\sqrt[3]{72}$

   A. $2\sqrt[3]{3}$

   B. $2\sqrt[3]{9}$

   C. 6

   D. $6\sqrt{2}$

8. Simplify: $\sqrt{\frac{16a^4}{b^6}}$

   A. $\frac{8a^2}{b^4}$

   B. $\frac{4a^2}{b^2}$

   C. $\frac{8a^2}{b^3}$

   D. $\frac{4a^2}{b^3}$

Laws of Exponents

A number in exponential form has a **base** and an **exponent**. The exponent indicates how many times the base is used as a factor.

In 5^4, the base is 5 and the exponent is 4. 5^4 indicates that 5 is used as a factor 4 times.

$$5^4 = 5 \cdot 5 \cdot 5 \cdot 5 = 625$$

Numbers in exponential form are sometimes called powers. The pattern in the examples below shows that when you multiply powers that have the same base, you add the exponents.

$$5^1 \cdot 5^1 = 5 \cdot 5 = 5^2 = 5^{1+1}$$
$$5^1 \cdot 5^2 = 5 \cdot (5 \cdot 5) = 5^3 = 5^{1+2}$$
$$5^2 \cdot 5^3 = (5 \cdot 5) \cdot (5 \cdot 5 \cdot 5) = 5^5 = 5^{2+3}$$

The next three examples show that when you raise a power to a power, you multiply the exponents.

$$(2^2)^2 = (2 \cdot 2) \cdot (2 \cdot 2) = 2^4 = 2^{2 \cdot 2}$$
$$(2^3)^2 = (2 \cdot 2 \cdot 2) \cdot (2 \cdot 2 \cdot 2) = 2^6 = 2^{3 \cdot 2}$$
$$(2^4)^2 = (2 \cdot 2 \cdot 2 \cdot 2) \cdot (2 \cdot 2 \cdot 2 \cdot 2) = 2^8 = 2^{4 \cdot 2}$$

If you extend each of these patterns, you will find that the observed exponent relationships always hold true. These patterns lead to generalizations about the properties of exponents, as defined in the box below. This process of observing patterns and using the patterns to make generalizations is called **inductive reasoning**.

The laws of exponents show how to simplify expressions in exponential form. The following box contains laws related to multiplication. In the laws below, a and b are real numbers and m and n are integers.

Product of Powers: To multiply powers with the same base, add the exponents.

$$a^m \cdot a^n = a^{m+n}$$

Power of a Power: To raise a number in exponential form to a power, multiply the exponents.

$$(a^m)^n = a^{mn}$$

Power of a Product: To find a power of a product, find the power of each factor and multiply.

$$(ab)^m = a^m b^m$$

Power of Zero: Any nonzero number raised to the power of zero is 1.

$$a^0 = 1, \text{ if } a \neq 0$$

Example 1

Simplify the expression $(x^3y^2z^0)^3$.

Strategy   **Apply the laws of exponents for multiplication.**

Step 1   Use the power of a product to rewrite the expression.

To find the power of a product, find the power of each factor and multiply.

$$(x^3y^2z^0)^3 = (x^3)^3(y^2)^3(z^0)^3$$

Step 2   Find the power of each power.

$$(x^3)^3(y^2)^3(z^0)^3$$

To raise a number in exponential form to a power, multiply the exponents.

$$(x^{3 \cdot 3})(y^{2 \cdot 3})(z^{0 \cdot 3})$$

$$(x^9)(y^6)(z^0)$$

Step 3   Apply the power of zero property.

Any nonzero number raised to the power of zero is 1.

$$(x^9)(y^6)(z^0)$$

$$(x^9)(y^6)(1)$$

$$x^9y^6$$

Solution   **The simplified form of $(x^3y^2z^0)^3$ is x^9y^6.**

The following box contains some laws of exponents that are related to division and reciprocals. Remember that a fraction indicates division. For example, $\frac{1}{2} = 1 \div 2$. In the laws below, a and b are real numbers and m and n are integers.

> **Quotient of Powers:** To find the quotient of powers with the same base, subtract the exponents.
>
> $$\frac{a^m}{a^n} = a^{m-n}, \text{ if } a \neq 0$$
>
> **Power of a Quotient:** To raise a quotient to a power, raise both the numerator and the denominator to that power.
>
> $$\left(\frac{a}{b}\right)^m = \frac{a^m}{b^m}, \text{ if } b \neq 0$$
>
> **Negative Powers and Reciprocals:** To change the sign of an exponent, move the expression to the denominator of a fraction.
>
> $$a^{-n} = \frac{1}{a^n}, \text{ if } a \neq 0$$
>
> To change the sign of an exponent in a denominator, move the expression to the numerator.
>
> $$\frac{1}{a^{-n}} = \frac{a^n}{1} = a^n, \text{ if } a \neq 0$$

Example 2

Simplify the expression $\left(\dfrac{x^4 y^5}{xy^2}\right)^2$.

Strategy   **Apply the laws of exponents.**

Step 1   Use the power of a quotient to rewrite the expression.

To raise a quotient to a power, raise both the numerator and denominator to that power.

$$\left(\dfrac{x^4 y^5}{xy^2}\right)^2 \rightarrow \dfrac{(x^4 y^5)^2}{(xy^2)^2}$$

Step 2   Find the power of each power.

$$\dfrac{(x^4)^2 (y^5)^2}{(x)^2 (y^2)^2}$$

To raise a number in exponential form to a power, multiply the exponents.

$$\dfrac{x^{4 \cdot 2} y^{5 \cdot 2}}{x^{1 \cdot 2} y^{2 \cdot 2}}$$

$$\dfrac{x^8 y^{10}}{x^2 y^4}$$

Step 3   Find the quotient of powers.

$$\dfrac{x^8 y^{10}}{x^2 y^4}$$

To find the quotient of powers with the same base, subtract the exponents.

$$x^{8-2} y^{10-4} \rightarrow x^6 y^6$$

Solution   The simplified form of $\left(\dfrac{x^4 y^5}{xy^2}\right)^2$ is $x^6 y^6$.

Example 3

Simplify: $6a^{-3}$, $a \neq 0$

Strategy   **Simplify using negative powers and reciprocals.**

Step 1   Write an equivalent expression for a^{-3} with a positive exponent.

To change the sign of an exponent, move the expression to the denominator of a fraction.

$$a^{-3} = \dfrac{1}{a^3}$$

Step 2   Write the simplified form of $6a^{-3}$.

$$6a^{-3} = 6\left(\dfrac{1}{a^3}\right) = \dfrac{6}{a^3}$$

Solution   The simplified form of $6a^{-3}$ is $\dfrac{6}{a^3}$.

The laws of exponents are also helpful for operations on numbers in scientific notation. A number is in **scientific notation** if it is written as the product of a power of 10 and a decimal number greater than or equal to 1 and less than 10.

The number 3.72×10^4 is written in scientific notation.

When multiplying or dividing numbers in scientific notation, first multiply or divide the decimal numbers. Then apply the laws of exponents to multiply or divide the powers of 10. In the equations below, A and B are the decimal numbers.

$$(A \times 10^m)(B \times 10^n) = AB \times 10^{m+n}$$

$$\frac{A \times 10^m}{B \times 10^n} = \frac{A}{B} \times 10^{m-n}, \text{ where } B \neq 0$$

Coached Example

Simplify: $\dfrac{a^4 b^{-3}}{a^{-2} b^2}$

The law for finding the quotient of powers states that to find the quotient of powers with the same base, _____ the exponents.

Simplify, using the law for finding the quotient of powers.

$a^{4 \underline{\quad} (-2)} b^{-3 \underline{\quad} 2}$

$a^{\underline{\quad}} b^{\underline{\quad}}$

Rewrite the expression so that all exponents are positive.

To change the sign of an exponent in the numerator, move the expression to the _____ of the fraction.

_____

The simplified form of $\dfrac{a^4 b^{-3}}{a^{-2} b^2}$ **is** _____.

Lesson Practice

Choose the correct answer.

1. Evaluate: $\left(\frac{5}{2}\right)^{-3}$

   A. $-\frac{125}{8}$

   B. $-\frac{6}{15}$

   C. $\frac{8}{125}$

   D. $\frac{125}{8}$

2. Simplify: $r^3 \cdot r^6$

   A. r^2

   B. r^3

   C. r^9

   D. r^{18}

3. Evaluate: $(7^0)^3$

   A. 1

   B. 3

   C. 21

   D. 343

4. Simplify: $a^{-7} \cdot a^4$, $a \neq 0$

   A. $\frac{1}{a^3}$

   B. $\frac{1}{a^{28}}$

   C. a^3

   D. a^{11}

5. Simplify: $\frac{8.4 \times 10^6}{2.8 \times 10^{-2}}$

   A. 3.0×10^{-4}

   B. 3.0×10^4

   C. 3.0×10^5

   D. 3.0×10^8

6. Simplify: $\frac{15x^8}{5x^2}$, $x \neq 0$

   A. $3x^4$

   B. $10x^4$

   C. $3x^6$

   D. $10x^6$

7. Simplify: $\left(\frac{2y^3}{x}\right)^4$

   A. $\frac{8y^7}{x^5}$

   B. $\frac{8y^{12}}{x^4}$

   C. $\frac{16y^7}{x^5}$

   D. $\frac{16y^{12}}{x^4}$

8. Simplify: $(-3m^4n)^2(6mn^{-5})$

   A. $\frac{54m^7}{n^{10}}$

   B. $\frac{54m^9}{n^3}$

   C. $\frac{-18m^7}{n^{10}}$

   D. $\frac{-18m^9}{n^3}$

Add and Subtract Polynomials

SOL: A.2.b

A **polynomial** is a term or expression that contains one or more variables or constants. **Terms** contain variables and/or numbers connected by multiplication and/or division. Some polynomials have specific names.

> A **monomial** is a polynomial with 1 term.   Example: $3x^2y$ is a monomial.
>
> A **binomial** is a polynomial with 2 terms.   Example: $2x - 5$ is a binomial.
>
> A **trinomial** is a polynomial with 3 terms.   Example: $2x^2 + 3x + 1$ is a trinomial.

You can model addition and subtraction of some polynomials with algebra tiles. When adding or subtracting with algebra tiles, using zero pairs may help you. Two tiles that have the same shape but different signs form a zero pair because the sum of the tiles is zero.

Example 1

Use algebra tiles to add the polynomials.

$(x^2 + 5x - 3) + (x + 7)$

Strategy   **Model each polynomial. Then combine the tiles and remove any zero pairs.**

Step 1   Model $x^2 + 5x - 3$.

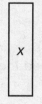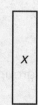

Step 2   Model $x + 7$.

Step 3 Combine the tiles, grouping tiles that have the same shape.

Remove any zero pairs.

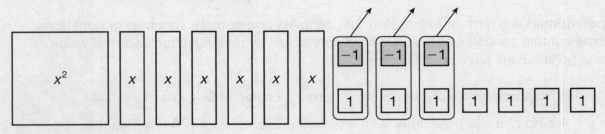

Step 4 Use the remaining tiles to write the sum.

There is one x^2 tile, six x tiles, and four 1 tiles.

$x^2 + 6x + 4$

Solution $(x^2 + 5x - 3) + (x + 7) = x^2 + 6x + 4$

Algebraically, polynomials can be simplified by combining like terms. **Like terms** contain the same variables raised to the same powers.

Examples: $3x$ and ^-6x are like terms. $^-2a^2b$ and $6a^2b$ are like terms.

$5x^2y^3$ and $3x^3y^2$ are not like terms.

To combine like terms, add or subtract their numerical coefficients, using the distributive property.

$3x + (^-6x) = (3 - 6)x = ^-3x$

$^-2a^2b + 6a^2b = (^-2 + 6)a^2b = 4a^2b$

To add polynomials, rewrite them so that like terms are grouped together. Then combine like terms.

Example 2

Add: $(a^2 - 6a + 1) + (3a^2 - 5a - 6)$

Strategy **Rewrite the expression so that like terms are grouped together. Then combine like terms.**

Step 1 Rewrite the expression so that like terms are grouped together.

$a^2 + 3a^2 - 6a - 5a + 1 - 6$

Step 2 Combine like terms.

$(a^2 + 3a^2) + (^-6a - 5a) + (1 - 6)$

$4a^2 - 11a - 5$

Solution $(a^2 - 6a + 1) + (3a^2 - 5a - 6) = 4a^2 - 11a - 5$

Example 3

Use algebra tiles to subtract the polynomials.

$$(3x^2 + 4x) - (x^2 + 2x)$$

Strategy **Model each polynomial. Then use shaded tiles to represent the tiles being subtracted, and remove all zero pairs.**

Step 1   Model $3x^2 + 4x$.

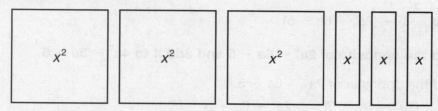

Step 2   Model $x^2 + 2x$.

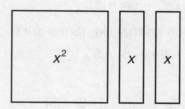

Step 3   Model the subtraction $(3x^2 + 4x) - (x^2 + 2x)$.

Subtract the one x^2 tile and two x tiles by showing them as shaded $-x^2$ and $-x$ tiles.

Remove any zero pairs.

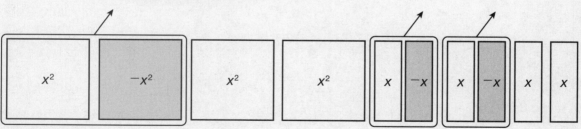

Step 4   Use the remaining tiles to write the difference.

There are two x^2 tiles and two x tiles remaining.

$2x^2 + 2x$

Solution $(3x^2 + 4x) - (x^2 + 2x) = 2x^2 + 2x$

To subtract polynomials algebraically, add the opposite, or negative, of the second polynomial. To find the opposite of a polynomial, change the sign of each term. This is the same as multiplying each term by $^-1$.

Examples: $-(-2a^2 - 3ab + 6) = 2a^2 + 3ab - 6$

$-(6x^2 + 4xy - 3y^2) = {}^-6x^2 - 4xy + 3y^2$

Example 4

Subtract: $(4a^2 - 3a - 6) - (2a^2 - 6a - 5)$

Strategy   **Find the opposite of $2a^2 - 6a - 5$ and add it to $4a^2 - 3a - 6$.**

Step 1   Find the opposite of $2a^2 - 6a - 5$.

$-(2a^2 - 6a - 5) = {}^-2a^2 + 6a + 5$

So, $(4a^2 - 3a - 6) - (2a^2 - 6a - 5)$ can be written as $4a^2 - 3a - 6 - 2a^2 + 6a + 5$.

Step 2   Rewrite the expression so that like terms are together.

$4a^2 - 2a^2 - 3a + 6a - 6 + 5$

Step 3   Combine like terms.

$(4a^2 - 2a^2) + (^-3a + 6a) + (^-6 + 5)$

$2a^2 + 3a - 1$

Solution   **$(4a^2 - 3a - 6) - (2a^2 - 6a - 5) = 2a^2 + 3a - 1$**

You can use what you know about adding polynomials to find the **perimeter** of, or the distance around, some polygons.

Coached Example

Find the perimeter of the triangle shown below.

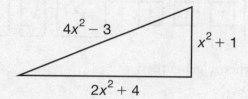

Recall that to find the perimeter of a polygon, add the lengths of all the sides.

P = _____ + _____ + _____

Next, rewrite the expression so that like terms are grouped together.

P = (_____ + _____ + _____) + (_____ + _____ + _____)

Now combine like terms to find an expression that represents the perimeter.

P = _____ + _____

The triangle has a perimeter of _____ units.

Choose the correct answer.

1. The algebra tiles below model the sum of two polynomials.

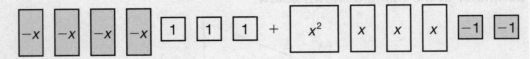

   Which sum is modeled by these algebra tiles?

   A. $(4x + 3) + (x^2 + 3x + 2)$

   B. $(^-4x + 3) + (x^2 + 3x + 2)$

   C. $(^-4x + 3) + (x^2 + 3x - 2)$

   D. $(^-4x - 3) + (x^2 + 3x - 2)$

2. Which set of algebra tiles models the solution to the following polynomial subtraction?

   $(2x^2 + 3x + 4) - (x^2 + x)$

   A. x^2 x^2 x^2 $-x$ $-x$ 1 1 1 1

   B. x^2 1 1 1 1

   C. x^2 x x 1 1 1 1

   D. $-x^2$ $-x^2$ x x x 1

3. Add: $(5x^2 - 2x) + (8x - 4)$

   A. $5x^2 + 6x - 4$

   B. $5x^2 + 6x + 4$

   C. $5x^2 + 10x - 4$

   D. $13x^2 - 6x$

4. Subtract:
$(9a^2 + 2ab - b^2) - (a^2 - 3ab + 2b^2)$

   A. $8a^2 - ab + b^2$

   B. $8a^2 - ab - 3b^2$

   C. $8a^2 + 5ab + b^2$

   D. $8a^2 + 5ab - 3b^2$

5. Which expression represents the perimeter, in units, of this pentagon?

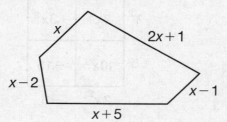

   A. $5x + 3$

   B. $6x + 3$

   C. $6x + 5$

   D. $6x + 9$

6. Add: $(^-2y^2 + 4y + 7) + (3y^2 - y)$

   A. $y^2 + 3y + 7$

   B. $y^2 + 5y + 7$

   C. $5y^2 + 3y + 7$

   D. $5y^2 + 5y + 7$

7. Subtract:
$(3x^3 + 4x^2 - 5) - (^-6x^3 + 7x^2 - 1)$

   A. $^-3x^3 - 3x^2 - 6$

   B. $9x^3 + 11x^2 - 6$

   C. $9x^3 - 3x^2 - 6$

   D. $9x^3 - 3x^2 - 4$

8. Subtract:
$(a^2b - 4ab + 8b) - (^-5ab^2 + ab)$

   A. $^-4a^2b - 3ab + 8b$

   B. $a^2b + 5ab^2 - 5ab + 8b$

   C. $6ab^2 - 5ab + 8b$

   D. $a^2b + 5ab^2 - 3ab + 8b$

Multiply Polynomials

SOL: A.2.b

Sometimes the lengths of the sides of a rectangle or square may be given as polynomials. If so, you can multiply those polynomials to find the **area** of the figure in square units. Remember:

Area of rectangle: $A = lw$, where l = length and w = width

Area of square: $A = s^2$, where s = side length

You can use an area model to help you multiply polynomials.

Example 1

This rectangle has a length of $2x^2 - 3$ units and a width of $x^2 + 5$ units. What is the area of the rectangle?

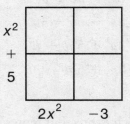

Strategy   **Use the area model.**

Step 1   Use the area model to multiply the polynomials.

First multiply the x^2 in $x^2 + 5$ by each term of the length.

$x^2 \cdot 2x^2 = 2x^4$

$x^2 \cdot {}^-3 = {}^-3x^2$

Then multiply the $+5$ in $x^2 + 5$ by each term of the length.

$5 \cdot 2x^2 = 10x^2$

$5 \cdot {}^-3 = {}^-15$

As you find each product, fill in the appropriate section of the model.

Step 2   Add the products in the model together, combining like terms.

$2x^4 - 3x^2 + 10x^2 - 15 = 2x^4 + 7x^2 - 15$

Solution   The area of the rectangle is $2x^4 + 7x^2 - 15$ square units.

To multiply a monomial by a polynomial algebraically, use the distributive property.

Distributive Property

The product of a factor and a sum is equal to the sum of the products of the factor and each addend. For all real numbers a, b, and c:

$$a(b + c) = ab + ac$$

$$a(b - c) = ab - ac$$

Example 2

Simplify: $4x^2y(3x + y - 8)$

Strategy   **Use the distributive property.**

Step 1   Multiply $4x^2y$ by each term in $(3x + y - 8)$.

$$4x^2y(3x + y - 8) = (4x^2y)(3x) + (4x^2y)(y) + (4x^2y)(-8)$$

Step 2   Simplify.

$$(4x^2y)(3x) = 12x^3y$$
$$(4x^2y)(y) = 4x^2y^2$$
$$(4x^2y)(-8) = -32x^2y$$

The full expression is $12x^3y + 4x^2y^2 - 32x^2y$.

Solution $4x^2y(3x + y - 8) = 12x^3y + 4x^2y^2 - 32x^2y$

Binomials can be multiplied in several ways. One method is called the **FOIL** method. FOIL stands for **F**irst, **O**uter, **I**nner, **L**ast.

The FOIL Method

Example: Multiply: $(x + 3)(x - 6)$

Multiply the **F**irst terms. $x \cdot x = x^2$

Multiply the **O**uter terms. $x \cdot {}^-6 = {}^-6x$

Multiply the **I**nner terms. $3 \cdot x = 3x$

Multiply the **L**ast terms. $3 \cdot {}^-6 = {}^-18$

Add the products. Combine like terms. $x^2 - 6x + 3x - 18$

$$x^2 - 3x - 18$$

Example 3

Multiply $(3x - 2)(x + 6)$ using FOIL.

Strategy   **Use the FOIL method to multiply two binomials.**

Step 1   Multiply the terms indicated by F-O-I-L.

Multiply the **F**irst terms: $3x \cdot x = 3x^2$

Multiply the **O**uter terms: $3x \cdot 6 = 18x$

Multiply the **I**nner terms: $^-2 \cdot x = {}^-2x$

Multiply the **L**ast terms: $^-2 \cdot 6 = {}^-12$

Step 2   Add the products and combine like terms.

$3x^2 + 18x - 2x - 12$

$3x^2 + 16x - 12$

Solution $(3x - 2)(x + 6) = 3x^2 + 16x - 12$

Note: Remember, the FOIL method works only when multiplying two binomials.

Another method you can use to multiply polynomials is writing out the multiplication vertically.

Example 4

What is the product of $(z^2 - 3z + 1)(5z + 2)$?

Strategy   **Set up a vertical multiplication problem. Then multiply each term in the trinomial by each term in the binomial.**

Step 1   Set up a vertical multiplication problem.

$$z^2 - 3z + 1$$
$$\times \quad\quad 5z + 2$$

Step 2   Multiply from right to left.

First multiply each term of the trinomial by 2.

$$z^2 - 3z + 1$$
$$\times \quad\quad 5z + 2$$
$$\overline{2z^2 - 6z + 2}$$

Step 3   Next multiply each term of the trinomial by $5z$.

Be sure to write like terms under like terms.

Then combine like terms to find the final product.

$$z^2 - 3z + 1$$
$$\times \quad\quad 5z + 2$$
$$\overline{2z^2 - 6z + 2}$$
$$+ \ 5z^3 - 15z^2 + 5z$$
$$\overline{5z^3 - 13z^2 - \ z + 2}$$

Solution   **The product is $5z^3 - 13z^2 - z + 2$.**

Coached Example

What is the product of $(3n + 5)$ and $(3n - 5)$?

Use the _____ method to multiply the two binomials.

Multiply the first term in $(3n + 5)$ by the first term in $(3n - 5)$: $3n \cdot 3n = $ _____

Multiply the first term in $(3n + 5)$ by the second term in $(3n - 5)$: $3n \cdot$ _____ $= $ _____

Multiply the second term in $(3n + 5)$ by the first term in $(3n - 5)$: $5 \cdot$ _____ $= $ _____

Multiply the second term in $(3n + 5)$ by the second term in $(3n - 5)$: $5 \cdot$ _____ $= $ _____

Add those products together, combining like terms:

_____ + _____ + _____ + _____ = _____

The product of $(3n + 5)$ and $(3n - 5)$ is _____.

Lesson Practice

Choose the correct answer.

1. Simplify: $2m(m^2 - 3m + 9)$

   A. $2m^3 - m + 9$

   B. $2m^3 - 6m + 18$

   C. $2m^3 - 6m^2 + 18$

   D. $2m^3 - 6m^2 + 18m$

2. Simplify: $(x - 4)(x + 5)$

   A. $x^2 + x + 20$

   B. $x^2 - x + 20$

   C. $x^2 + x - 20$

   D. $x^2 + 5x - 20$

3. Each side of a square is $3x - 5$ units long. What is the area, in square units, of the square?

   A. $12x - 20$

   B. $9x^2 + 25$

   C. $9x^2 - 15x + 25$

   D. $9x^2 - 30x + 25$

4. Simplify: $^-ab(a^2 + 4a - 8)$

   A. $^-a^3b - 4a^2b - 8ab$

   B. $^-a^3b - 4a^2b + 8ab$

   C. $^-a^3b + 4a^2b - 8ab$

   D. $^-a^3b + 4a^2b + 8ab$

5. A rectangle has a length of $x^2 + 1$ units and a width of $x + 6$ units. What is the area, in square units, of the rectangle?

   A. $x^2 + x + 7$

   B. $x^3 + x + 6$

   C. $x^3 + 6x^2 + 6x$

   D. $x^3 + 6x^2 + x + 6$

6. Simplify: $(6x + 2)(3x - 2)$

   A. $18x^2 - 18x - 4$

   B. $18x^2 - 6x - 4$

   C. $18x^2 - 4$

   D. $18x^2 + 6x - 4$

7. Simplify: $(a - 4)(2a^2 - a + 7)$

   A. $^-6a^2 + 3a - 21$

   B. $2a^3 - 9a^2 + 11a - 28$

   C. $2a^3 - 8a^2 + 3a - 28$

   D. $2a^3 - a^2 + 7a - 4$

8. Simplify: $(8x^2 - 3x - 1)(2x + 3)$

   A. $16x^3 + 18x^2 - 11x - 3$

   B. $16x^3 + 18x^2 - 7x - 3$

   C. $16x^3 - 6x^2 - 2x - 3$

   D. $16x^3 - 30x^2 - 11x - 3$

Factor Polynomials

SOL: A.2.c

Factoring means writing a number or polynomial as the product of its factors. These factors are numbers and/or polynomials that produce the original number or polynomial when multiplied. For example, the factored form of the number 10 is 2×5. When you factor a polynomial, you write the polynomial as the product of other polynomials. Factoring reverses polynomial multiplication.

The first step in factoring a polynomial is to find the **greatest common factor (GCF)** of all the terms. For example, the greatest common factor of $8x^3 - 32x^2 + 12x$ is $4x$, because this is the greatest factor of $8x^3$, $-32x^2$, and $12x$. When $4x$ is factored out of each term, the result is the factored form of the polynomial: $4x(2x^2 - 8x + 3)$. You must find the GCF so that the polynomial is fully factored.

Example 1

What is the greatest common factor of $36y^3z$ and $81y^2z^2$?

Strategy **Identify the greatest monomial that evenly divides both terms.**

> **Step 1** Identify the GCF of the coefficients.
>
> The GCF of 36 and 81 is 9.

> **Step 2** Identify the GCFs of the variables.
>
> The GCF of y^3 and y^2 is y^2.
>
> The GCF of z and z^2 is z.

> **Step 3** Multiply these three GCFs together.
>
> $9 \cdot y^2 \cdot z = 9y^2z$

Solution **The greatest common factor of $36y^3z$ and $81y^2z^2$ is $9y^2z$.**

A trinomial is a polynomial with three terms. When you factor a trinomial, the result may be the product of two binomials. If the trinomial has the form $x^2 + bx + c$, look for two factors of c (the third term) whose sum is b (the coefficient of the second term).

After you have factored a trinomial, you can always use the FOIL method or a graphing calculator to check your work.

Example 2

Factor: $x^2 + 5x + 6$

Strategy **Look for two factors of 6 whose sum is 5.**

Step 1 List factor pairs of 6 and their sums until you find the correct pair.

Factors of 6	Sum of Factors = 5?
1, 6	$1 + 6 = 7$ No.
$^-1, ^-6$	$^-1 + (^-6) = ^-7$ No.
2, 3	$2 + 3 = 5$ Yes.

The factors 2 and 3 have a sum of 5, so use 2 and 3 as the factors of c in $x^2 + bx + c$.

Step 2 Write $x^2 + 5x + 6$ as the product of two binomials.

$(x + 2)(x + 3)$

Step 3 Use the FOIL method to check $(x + 2)(x + 3)$.

First: $x \cdot x = x^2$

Outer: $x \cdot 3 = 3x$

Inner: $2 \cdot x = 2x$

Last: $2 \cdot 3 = 6$

$(x + 2)(x + 3) = x^2 + 3x + 2x + 6 = x^2 + 5x + 6$ ✓

Solution $x^2 + 5x + 6 = (x + 2)(x + 3)$

When factoring a trinomial of the form $ax^2 + bx + c$, use trial and error.

Example 3

Factor: $2x^2 - x - 15$

Strategy Choose factors of 2 and $^-15$. Write the polynomial as a product of two binomials using these factors, and check to see if you get the correct middle term.

Step 1 Find the factors of 2 and $^-15$.

Factors of 2	Factors of $^-15$	
1, 2	$^-1$, 15	1, $^-15$
$^-1$, $^-2$	$^-3$, 5	3, $^-5$

Step 2 Substitute the factors from Step 1 to form trial binomial factors until you get factors that will give the correct middle term.

Trial Factors	Middle Term = ^-x?
$(x - 1)(2x + 15)$	$15x - 2x = 13x$ No.
$(^-1x - 1)(^-2x + 15)$	$^-15x + 2x = ^-13x$ No.
$(x - 3)(2x + 5)$	$5x - 6x = ^-x$ Yes.

Step 3 Use the trial factors that give the correct middle term.

$(x - 3)(2x + 5)$

Step 4 Use a graphing calculator to check your solution.

Store any positive one-digit integer value (not 0 or 1) in x. For example, to store a 4, type 4 STO➜ x.

Hit ENTER.

Type in $2x^2 - x - 15 = (x - 3)(2x + 5)$.

To find the "=" sign, hit 2nd MATH to access the TEST menu and select "1: =."

Now hit ENTER.

If a 0 appears, this is not the correct answer. If a 1 appears, this is the correct answer. Since a 1 appears, the polynomial is correctly factored.

Solution $2x^2 - x - 15 = (x - 3)(2x + 5)$

Here are some helpful rules for signs when factoring a trinomial into two binomials.

$ax^2 + bx + c \rightarrow (\ + \ )(\ + \ )$

$ax^2 - bx + c \rightarrow (\ - \ )(\ - \ )$

$ax^2 + bx - c \rightarrow (\ + \ )(\ - \ )$ or $(\ - \ )(\ + \ )$

$ax^2 - bx - c \rightarrow (\ + \ )(\ - \ )$ or $(\ - \ )(\ + \ )$

If a binomial is the **difference of two squares**, its factors are the sum of the square roots of the terms and the difference of the square roots of the terms. For the numbers a and b, $a^2 - b^2 = (a + b)(a - b)$. For example, $x^2 - 2^2 = (x + 2)(x - 2)$.

Example 4

Factor: $6x^2 - 96$

Strategy   **Look for a GCF. Then factor the remaining binomial.**

Step 1   Find the greatest common factor.

The GCF of $6x^2$ and 96 is 6.

$6x^2 - 96 = 6(x^2 - 16)$

Step 2   Factor $x^2 - 16$.

$x^2 - 16$ is the difference of two squares. So its factors are the sum of the square roots of x^2 and 16 and the difference of their square roots.

$x^2 - 16 = x^2 - 4^2 = (x + 4)(x - 4)$

Step 3   Write the factored form of $6x^2 - 96$.

$6x^2 - 96 = 6(x^2 - 16) = 6(x + 4)(x - 4)$

Step 4   Use a graphing calculator to check your solution.

Store any positive one-digit integer value (not 0 or 1) in x and press ENTER.

Type in $6x^2 - 96 = 6(x + 4)(x - 4)$ and press ENTER.

Since a 1 appears, the polynomial is correctly factored.

Solution $6x^2 - 96 = 6(x + 4)(x - 4)$

All of the polynomials you have seen so far in this lesson have been factorable. Some polynomials, however, are not factorable. These are called **prime polynomials**. Below are some examples of prime polynomials along with the reason that each cannot be factored.

Prime Polynomial	Reason
$a^2 + 49$	The sum of two squares, $x^2 + y^2$, is always prime.
$3x + 5$	$3x$ and 5 have no common factors.
$x^2 - 4x + 10$	No factor pairs of 10 have a sum of $^-4$.

Example 5

Is $x^2 + 3x - 5$ a prime polynomial?

Strategy   **Look for two factors of $^-5$ whose sum is 3.**

Step 1   List factor pairs of $^-5$ and their sums.

Factors of $^-5$	Sum of Factors
$^-1, 5$	$^-1 + 5 = 4$ No.
$1, ^-5$	$1 + (^-5) = ^-4$ No.

Step 2   Determine if the polynomial can be factored.

Neither of the factor pairs of $^-5$ has a sum of 3.

The polynomial cannot be factored as a product of two binomials.

Solution $x^2 + 3x - 5$ **is a prime polynomial. It cannot be factored.**

Coached Example

Factor: $4m^2 - 25n^2$

Are there any common factors? _____.

The expression is the _____ of two squares.

The factored form is the _____ of the square roots of the terms times the _____ of their square roots.

The square root of $4m^2$ is _____.

The square root of $25n^2$ is _____.

In factored form, $4m^2 - 25n^2 = ($_____$)($_____$)$.

Choose the correct answer.

1. Factor: $6a^2 + 18ab$

    A. $a(6a + 3b)$

    B. $6(a + 18b)$

    C. $6a(a + 3b)$

    D. $6a(a + 18b)$

2. Factor: $x^2 - 3x - 28$

    A. $(x + 7)(x - 4)$

    B. $(x + 4)(x - 7)$

    C. $(x + 2)(x - 14)$

    D. $(x - 4)(x - 7)$

3. Factor: $n^2 - 100$

    A. $n(n - 100)$

    B. $(n + 100)(n - 1)$

    C. $(n + 10)(n - 10)$

    D. $(n - 10)(n - 10)$

4. Which of the following is a prime polynomial?

    A. $4x^2 + 9$

    B. $2x^2 + 16x$

    C. $49x^2 - 1$

    D. $x^2 - 11x + 24$

5. Factor: $x^2 + 8x + 12$

    A. $(x + 4)(x + 3)$

    B. $(x + 12)(x + 1)$

    C. $(x + 6)(x + 2)$

    D. The expression cannot be factored.

6. Factor: $8y^2 - 32$

    A. $8y(y - 4)$

    B. $8(y + 2)(y - 2)$

    C. $8(y + 4)(y - 4)$

    D. The expression cannot be factored.

7. Factor: $3x^2 + 11x - 4$

    A. $(3x - 4)(x + 1)$

    B. $(3x - 2)(x + 2)$

    C. $(3x - 1)(x + 4)$

    D. $(3x + 1)(x - 4)$

8. Factor: $a^2 - 13a + 10$

    A. $(a - 10)(a - 1)$

    B. $(a + 5)(a - 2)$

    C. $(a - 10)(a - 3)$

    D. The expression cannot be factored.

Divide Polynomials

SOL: A.2b

You've learned to use an area model to help you multiply polynomials. You can also use an area model to help you divide polynomials to find a missing length in a rectangle.

Example 1

A rectangle has a width of $a - 6$ units and an area of $a^2 - 5a - 6$ square units. What is the length of the rectangle?

Strategy   **Use an area model.**

Step 1   Draw an area model.

Draw a rectangle. Write the width vertically. Since $a - 6$ involves subtraction, write the minus sign next to the 6 so you remember to multiply by $^-6$.

Write the first term of the area, a^2, in the top left section of the model.

Write the last term of the area, $^-6$, in the bottom right section of the model.

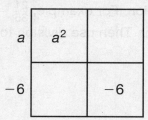

Step 2   Use the area model to find the first and second terms of the length.

Ask yourself, what number or variable multiplied by a, gives a product of a^2?

$a \cdot a = a^2$, so a must be the first term in the length.

Ask yourself, what number or variable, multiplied by $^-6$, gives a product of $^-6$?

$^-6 \cdot 1 = {}^-6$, so 1 must be the second term in the length.

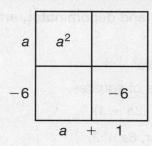

Step 3   Check your answer.

Find the products for the remaining sections of the model to check your answer.

$$1 \cdot a = a$$
$$a \cdot {}^-6 = {}^-6a$$

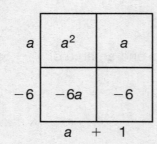

If $a + 1$ is the length, the area is $a^2 + a - 6a - 6 = a^2 - 5a - 6$.

That is the correct area, so $a + 1$ is the correct length.

Solution   **The length of the rectangle is $a + 1$ units.**

Recall that a fraction represents division. For example, $\frac{21}{35} = 21\overline{)35}$. To simplify the fraction, factor the numerator and denominator. Then use division to cancel the common factors.

$$\frac{21}{35} = \frac{3 \times \overset{1}{\cancel{7}}}{5 \times \underset{1}{\cancel{7}}} = \frac{3}{5}$$

The same process of factoring and canceling common factors also works for dividing polynomials. Be sure to factor both the numerator and the denominator completely before canceling out any common factors.

Example 2

Simplify: $\frac{9a^2 - 1}{6a + 2}$, $a \neq \frac{-1}{3}$

Strategy   **Factor the numerator and denominator, and then cancel out common factors.**

Step 1   Factor the numerator, $9a^2 - 1$.

This is a difference of squares.

$$9a^2 - 1 = (3a + 1)(3a - 1)$$

Step 2   Factor the denominator, $6a + 2$.

2 is a common factor of both terms.

$$6a + 2 = 2(3a + 1)$$

Step 3 Rewrite the expression with the factored numerator and denominator. Cancel out any common factors.

$$\frac{9a^2 - 1}{6a + 2} = \frac{(3a + 1)(3a - 1)}{2(3a + 1)}$$

The numerator and denominator have the common factor $(3a + 1)$.

$$\frac{\cancel{(3a + 1)}(3a - 1)}{2\cancel{(3a + 1)}} = \frac{3a - 1}{2}$$

Solution $\dfrac{9a^2 - 1}{6a + 2} = \dfrac{3a - 1}{2}$

If the numerator contains a polynomial with an exponent greater than 2, you can use grouping to factor the expression. First factor out the GCF, if there is one, and then group terms with common factors. Then factor the common factor from each group of terms to see if you can identify a binomial factor of the entire polynomial.

Example 3

Simplify: $\dfrac{x^3 + 7x^2 - x - 7}{x^2 - 1}$, $x \neq {}^-1, 1$

Strategy **Use grouping to factor the numerator.**

Step 1 Group the terms in the numerator.

$$x^3 + 7x^2 - x - 7 \rightarrow (x^3 + 7x^2) + ({}^-x - 7)$$

Step 2 Factor x^2 from the first two terms and $^-1$ from the last two terms of the numerator.

$$(x^3 + 7x^2) + ({}^-x - 7) \rightarrow x^2(x + 7) - 1(x + 7)$$

Step 3 Apply the distributive property.

Since $(x + 7)$ is a factor of each term, you can factor it out.

$$x^2(x + 7) - 1(x + 7) \rightarrow (x + 7)(x^2 - 1)$$

Step 4 Find the quotient using the factored form of the numerator.

$$\frac{(x + 7)(x^2 - 1)}{x^2 - 1}$$

The numerator and denominator have a common factor of $x^2 - 1$, so those cancel out.

$$\frac{(x + 7)\cancel{(x^2 - 1)}}{\cancel{x^2 - 1}} = x + 7$$

Solution $\dfrac{x^3 + 7x^2 - x - 7}{x^2 - 1} = x + 7$

Another way to divide polynomials is to write a long division problem.

Example 4

Find the quotient: $a - 4 \overline{)a^2 + 3a - 28}$, $a \neq {}^-7, 4$

Strategy   **Use the steps of long division: divide, multiply, subtract, and bring down.**

Step 1   Start by dividing the first term in the dividend, a^2, by the first term in the divisor, a.

$$a^2 \div a = a^2 \div a^1 = a^{2-1} = a^1 = a$$

So write a in the quotient.

$$\begin{array}{r} a \\ a - 4 \overline{)a^2 + 3a - 28} \end{array}$$

Step 2   Multiply the divisor, $a - 4$, by the first term in the quotient, a.

$$a(a - 4) = (a \cdot a) - (a \cdot 4) = a^2 - 4a$$

Write $a^2 - 4a$ under the dividend, like this:

$$\begin{array}{r} a \\ a - 4 \overline{)a^2 + 3a - 28} \\ a^2 - 4a \end{array}$$

Step 3   Subtract.

Remember, subtracting $(a^2 - 4a)$ is the same as adding the opposite of $a^2 - 4a$. So change all the signs in $a^2 - 4a$ and then add like terms.

$$\begin{array}{r} a \\ a - 4 \overline{)a^2 + 3a - 28} \\ {}^-a^2 + 4a \\ \hline 7a \end{array}$$

Step 4   Bring down the next term, $- 28$.

$$\begin{array}{r} a \\ a - 4 \overline{)a^2 + 3a - 28} \\ {}^-a^2 + 4a \downarrow \\ \hline 7a - 28 \end{array}$$

Step 5   Repeat the steps: divide, multiply, subtract, and bring down.

$$
\require{enclose}
\begin{array}{r}
a \quad\quad\;\; + 7 \\
a - 4 \enclose{longdiv}{a^2 + 3a - 28} \\
\underline{-a^2 + 4a} \quad\;\downarrow \\
7a - 28 \\
\underline{-7a + 28} \\
0
\end{array}
$$

Solution   **The quotient is $a + 7$.**

When you divide a polynomial by a monomial, you can break the fraction into multiple fractions, dividing each term in the numerator by the denominator.

Coached Example

Simplify: $\dfrac{8x^3 + 2x - 4}{2x}$ **, $x \neq 0$**

Rewrite the fraction as three separate fractions.

$$\frac{8x^3 + 2x - 4}{2x} = \frac{}{2x} + \frac{}{2x} - \frac{}{2x}$$

Using the quotient of powers rule, fully simplify the first fraction.

Simplify the second fraction.

Simplify the third fraction, keeping a positive exponent for the x-term.

The quotient $\dfrac{8x^3 + 2x - 4}{2x}$ in simplified form is _____.

Lesson Practice

Choose the correct answer.

1. Simplify: $\dfrac{(x-8)(x-8)}{(x+4)(x-8)}$, $x \neq {}^-4, 8$

   A. $x + 4$

   B. $\dfrac{1}{x+4}$

   C. $\dfrac{x-2}{x+4}$

   D. $\dfrac{x-8}{x+4}$

2. Simplify: $\dfrac{12a^2b - 9ab + 15b}{3ab}$, $a \neq 0, b \neq 0$

   A. $4a^2 - 3 + 5b$

   B. $4a - 3ab + 5b$

   C. $4a - 3 + \dfrac{5}{a}$

   D. $4a - 3 + \dfrac{5b}{a}$

3. What is this quotient?

   $x + 4\overline{)x^2 - 2x - 24}$, $x \neq {}^-4, 6$

   A. $x - 6$

   B. $x - 2$

   C. $x + 2$

   D. $x + 6$

4. A rectangle has a length of $2n + 3$ units and an area of $2n^2 - 5n - 12$ square units. What is its width, in units?

   A. $n - 4$

   B. $n - 2$

   C. $n + 2$

   D. $n + 4$

5. Simplify: $\dfrac{a^2 - 5a + 4}{a - 1}$, $a \neq 1$

   A. $a - 5$

   B. $a - 4$

   C. $a + 4$

   D. $a + 5$

6. Simplify: $(18x^2y^3 + 8xy^2z) \div 2xy^2$, $x \neq 0$, $y \neq 0$

   A. $9xy + 4$

   B. $9xy + 4z$

   C. $9x^2y + 4$

   D. $9x^2y + 4z$

7. Simplify: $\dfrac{x^3 - 3x^2 + 4x - 12}{x^2 + 4}$

   A. $x - 4$

   B. $x - 3$

   C. $x + 3$

   D. $x + 4$

8. What is this quotient?

   $x + 5\overline{)2x^2 + 9x - 5}$, $x \neq {}^-5, \dfrac{1}{2}$

   A. $x - 1$

   B. $x + 4$

   C. $2x - 1$

   D. $2x + 4$

Write Algebraic Expressions

SOL: A.1

Recall that an algebraic expression is a combination of numbers and variables that are connected by one or more operations. To translate phrases or word problems into algebraic expressions, use key words to help you decide which operation or operations to use in the expression you write.

Key Words

Addition	Multiplication	Subtraction	Division
plus	times	less	divided by
more than	twice	less than	quotient
increased by	of	fewer than	share equally
additional	product	decreased by	separate into
sum	per	difference	equal groups

Example 1

Express the following phrase as an algebraic expression: the sum of three times the quantity of a number increased by six, and one-half of the same number. Be sure to define the variable you choose.

Strategy **Use key words to translate the words into an algebraic expression.**

Step 1 Identify and interpret the key words.

The word "sum" indicates addition.

The words "three times" indicate multiplying by 3.

The words "quantity of a number increased by six" indicate that 6 is added to an unknown number.

The words "one-half of" indicate multiplying the unknown number by $\frac{1}{2}$.

Step 2 Translate the words into an algebraic expression.

Let n represent the unknown number.

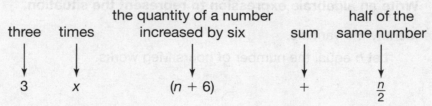

three	times	the quantity of a number increased by six	sum	half of the same number
3	x	$(n + 6)$	$+$	$\frac{n}{2}$

Parentheses are needed because 3 is multiplied by the quantity $(n + 6)$, not just by n.

Solution **The phrase can be represented by $3 \times (n + 6) + \frac{n}{2}$ or $3(n + 6) + \frac{n}{2}$.**

You can also use key words to translate real-world problems into algebraic expressions. Remember that key words do not appear in every word problem. Always consider whether the expression you write makes sense for the given situation.

Example 2

At the deli, Omar bought a loaf of bread for $3.19. He also bought 3.5 pounds of turkey at a cost of x dollars per pound. Write an expression that represents the total cost of these items.

Strategy **Use key words to translate the words into an algebraic expression.**

Step 1 Use key words and other clues to interpret the problem.

Each pound of turkey costs the same amount. So the cost of the turkey can be found by multiplying each pound by the price per pound. (The key word "per" means multiplication.)

The key word "total" indicates using either addition or multiplication. In this case, the total cost is made up of the cost of the bread and the cost of the turkey, so it makes sense to add them.

Step 2 Translate the words into an algebraic expression.

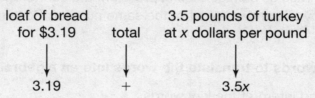

loaf of bread for $3.19	total	3.5 pounds of turkey at x dollars per pound
3.19	+	3.5x

Solution **The expression representing the total cost, in dollars, is 3.19 + 3.5x.**

Example 3

Meg works at a small electronics store and earns a base salary of $25 each week. She also earns $16 for each hour she works. Let h represent the number of hours Meg works in one week. Write an expression that represents Meg's weekly pay.

Strategy **Write an algebraic expression to represent the situation.**

Step 1 Identify the variable.

Let h equal the number of hours Meg works.

Step 2   Write an algebraic expression.

Meg earns $16 for each hour she works, so 16h represents the amount Meg earns for working h hours.

Meg also earns a base salary of $25 each week, so you must add $25 to her hourly earnings.

16h + 25 represents the amount Meg earns for h hours worked plus her base salary.

Solution   The expression 16h + 25 represents Meg's weekly pay, in dollars.

Coached Example

Express the following phrase as an algebraic expression: twice the quantity of a number decreased by seven is divided by one-fourth of the same number.

Identify and interpret the key words.

The word "_____" indicates multiplying by 2.

The words "quantity of a number decreased by 7" indicate _____ 7 from an unknown number.

The words "is divided by" indicate _____.

"One-fourth of" the same number indicates _____ the unknown number by $\frac{1}{4}$.

Choose a variable to represent the unknown number.

Let x represent the unknown number.

Translate the sentence into an algebraic expression.

| twice | the quantity of a number decreased by seven | is divided by | one-fourth of the same number |

_____   (_____)   _____   _____

The sentence can be represented as _____.

Lesson Practice

Choose the correct answer.

1. Which expression represents "four less than six times the quantity of a number increased by seven"?

   A. $4 - 6n + 7$

   B. $4 - 6(n + 7)$

   C. $6n + 7 - 4$

   D. $6(n + 7) - 4$

2. Which expression represents "the product of twice a number and one less than that same number"?

   A. $n(2n - 1)$ C. $2n(n - 1)$

   B. $n^2 - 1$ D. $2n \cdot n - 1$

3. Yoshi shares a package of cookies equally between four friends and herself. If the package contains c cookies, which expression shows how many cookies each friend receives?

   A. $c \div 5$ C. $c + 5$

   B. $5c$ D. $c - 5$

4. Last week, Adam worked on his science experiment for x hours per day, Monday through Thursday, and for 4 hours over the weekend. Which expression represents the total number of hours he spent working on his science experiment last week?

   A. $x + 4$ C. $4(x + 4)$

   B. $4x + 4$ D. $\frac{x}{4} + 4$

5. Which expression represents "eight more than half a number decreased by three"?

   A. $8 - \frac{1}{2} - 3n$ C. $8 - \frac{n}{2} - 3$

   B. $8 + \frac{1}{2} - 3n$ D. $8 + \frac{n}{2} - 3$

6. Which expression represents "five times the quotient of a number and six"?

   A. $5(n + 6)$ C. $5n \div 6$

   B. $5(n \div 6)$ D. $5 \div (n + 6)$

7. Four friends shared three orders of oysters at a restaurant. Each order contained x oysters, and each person ate the same number of oysters. Which expression represents the number of oysters each person ate?

   A. $\frac{3x}{4}$

   B. $\frac{3 \cdot 4}{x}$

   C. $\frac{4x}{3}$

   D. $\frac{x}{3 \cdot 4}$

8. Adina reads 20 pages per day in a 340-page book. Which expression represents how many pages she has left to read after d days?

   A. $20d$

   B. $340 + 20d$

   C. $340 - (20 + d)$

   D. $340 - 20d$

Evaluate Algebraic Expressions

SOL: A.1

To evaluate an algebraic expression for given values of the variables, substitute the defined value for each variable and then evaluate. When multiple operations are indicated in an algebraic expression, you must follow the **order of operations** when evaluating the expression.

> ### Order of Operations
> First, perform all operations inside parentheses and other grouping symbols.
>
> Then, simplify all exponents (including roots).
>
> Next, multiply and divide in order from left to right.
>
> Finally, add and subtract in order from left to right.

Example 1

What is the value of $3x - x^2$ when $x = {}^-6$?

Strategy   **Substitute $^-6$ for x and apply the order of operations.**

Step 1   Substitute $^-6$ for x.

$3x - x^2$ becomes $3(^-6) - (^-6)^2$.

Step 2   Evaluate the exponent.

$(^-6)^2 = (^-6) \times (^-6) = 36$

The expression becomes $3(^-6) - 36$.

Step 3   Multiply.

$3(^-6) = {}^-18$

The expression becomes $^-18 - 36$.

Step 4   Subtract.

$^-18 - 36 = {}^-54$

Solution   **The value of $3x - x^2$ when $x = {}^-6$ is $^-54$.**

Example 2

What is the value of $-4g^3h^2$ when $g = 2$ and $h = 4$?

Strategy **Substitute the values for the variables. Then evaluate.**

Step 1 Substitute 2 for g and 4 for h.

$$-4g^3h^2$$
$$-4(2)^3(4)^2$$

Step 2 Apply the order of operations.

$-4(2)^3(4)^2$	Simplify exponents.
$-4(8)(16)$	Multiply in order from left to right.
$-32(16)$	Multiply again.
-512	

Solution **When $g = 2$ and $h = 4$, the value of $-4g^3h^2$ is -512.**

Example 3

What is the value of $2 \times |x^2 + 1|$ when $x = -8$?

Strategy **Substitute the value of the variable and evaluate the expression.**

Step 1 Substitute -8 for x.

$$2 \times |x^2 + 1|$$
$$2 \times |(-8)^2 + 1|$$

Step 2 Apply the order of operations.

Since the absolute value is a grouping symbol, simplify the absolute value first. Use the order of operations to simplify the expression in the absolute value.

$|(-8)^2 + 1|$	Simplify the exponent.
$|64 + 1|$	Add from left to right.
$|65|$	The absolute value of any number is nonnegative.
65	

Step 3 Multiply.

$$2 \times |(-8)^2 + 1| = 2 \times 65 = 130$$

Solution **When $x = -8$, the value of the expression $2 \times |x^2 + 1|$ is 130.**

Example 4

What is the value of $\sqrt{3^2 a^4 b^2}$ when $a = 2$ and $b = 6$?

Strategy   **Substitute the values of the variables and evaluate the expression.**

Step 1   Substitute 2 for a and 6 for b.

$$\sqrt{3^2 a^4 b^2}$$
$$\sqrt{(3^2)(2^4)(6^2)}$$

Step 2   Apply the order of operations.

Perform the operations inside the grouping symbols first. The square root is a grouping symbol, so simplify the radicand.

$\sqrt{(3^2)(2^4)(6^2)}$	Simplify exponents.
$\sqrt{(9)(16)(36)}$	Multiply from left to right.
$\sqrt{5,184}$	

Step 3   Use your calculator to find the square root.

$$\sqrt{5,184} = 72$$

Solution   **When $a = 2$ and $b = 6$, the value of the expression $\sqrt{3^2 a^4 b^2}$ is 72.**

Example 5

The weight, in ounces, of Kyle's new puppy can be found using the algebraic expression $2t + 7$, where t represents the age of the puppy in weeks. Use this expression to find the weight of the puppy when it is 12 weeks old.

Strategy   **Substitute the age of the puppy into the expression. Then simplify.**

Step 1   Substitute the age of the puppy into the expression.

The variable t represents the age of the puppy in weeks.

When the puppy is 12 weeks old, $t = 12$.

Substituting this into the expression $2t + 7$ gives $2(12) + 7$.

Step 2   Evaluate the expression.

$2(12) + 7$	Multiply.
$24 + 7$	Add.
31	

The weight of the puppy is 31 ounces.

Solution   **When Kyle's puppy is 12 weeks old, it weighs 31 ounces.**

A fraction bar is another grouping symbol, since it groups the numerator and denominator together without using parentheses. When an expression contains an algebraic fraction, use the order of operations to simplify the numerator and to simplify the denominator. Then divide or cancel common factors if possible.

Coached Example

What is the value of $\frac{4 + x}{4 - x} + \sqrt[3]{x}$ when $x = 8$?

Substitute _____ for x in the expression.

$$\frac{4 +}{4 -} + \sqrt[3]{}$$

First, simplify the expression in the numerator of the fraction.

$$\frac{}{4 -} + \sqrt[3]{}$$

Next, simplify the expression in the denominator of the fraction.

$$\frac{}{} + \sqrt[3]{}$$

Take the cube root.

_____ + _____

Simplify the fraction.

_____ + _____

Finally, add.

_____

When $x = 8$, the value of the expression $\frac{4 + x}{4 - x} + \sqrt[3]{x}$ is _____.

Lesson Practice

Choose the correct answer.

1. What is the value of $5g - 3h$ when $g = {}^-4$ and $h = 10$?

   A. $^-50$
   B. $^-10$
   C. 38
   D. 50

2. What is the value of $|x^2 - 5x| + 1$ when $x = 3$?

   A. $^-5$
   B. 5
   C. 7
   D. 24

3. What is the value of $2x^3y^2$ when $x = {}^-2$ and $y = 3$?

   A. $^-216$
   B. $^-144$
   C. 144
   D. 216

4. What is the value of $\sqrt{4a^2 - 20}$ when $a = 3$?

   A. $^-14$
   B. $2\sqrt{3}$
   C. 4
   D. 16

5. What is the value of $\frac{x^2 + 15}{x + 3}$ when $x = 5$?

   A. 3
   B. 5
   C. 10
   D. 11

6. What is the value of $|{}^-x + 5y| + \sqrt{xy}$ when $x = 12$ and $y = 3$?

   A. 3
   B. 9
   C. 16
   D. 33

7. The weight, in pounds, of a wheelbarrow containing b bricks is given by the expression $60 + 5b$. What is the total weight of the wheelbarrow when it holds 20 bricks?

   A. 80 pounds
   B. 85 pounds
   C. 160 pounds
   D. 1,300 pounds

8. Carla uses the expression $10x - 7.5$ to calculate the total amount of money, in dollars, she earns from mowing her neighbor's lawn x times. If she mowed her neighbor's lawn 8 times during the summer, how much money did she earn?

   A. $87.50
   B. $80.00
   C. $75.00
   D. $72.50

Chapter 1 Review

1. Simplify: $(1.5 \times 10^4)(3.0 \times 10^{-8})$

   A. 4.5×10^{-2}

   B. 4.5×10^{-4}

   C. 4.5×10^{-12}

   D. 4.5×10^{-32}

2. A quadrilateral is shown below.

   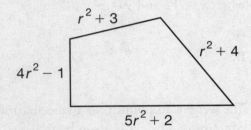

   Which expression represents the perimeter of this quadrilateral?

   A. $9r^2 + 8$

   B. $11r^2 + 8$

   C. $11r^2 + 10$

   D. $9r^2 + 2r + 10$

3. What is the value of $\sqrt{\dfrac{16}{169}}$?

   A. $\dfrac{1}{9}$

   B. $\dfrac{1}{4}$

   C. $\dfrac{4}{14}$

   D. $\dfrac{4}{13}$

4. The cost, in dollars, for downloading music from an online music company is given by the expression $15d + 4$, where d represents the number of CDs downloaded. How much does it cost to download 4 CDs from this company?

   A. $23

   B. $60

   C. $64

   D. $120

5. Factor: $6ab^2 - 3ab + 24a$

   A. $3a(2b^2 - b + 8)$

   B. $3a(2b + 4)(b - 2)$

   C. $3ab(2b - 1 + 8)$

   D. $6ab(b - 2 + 4a)$

6. Simplify: $(3x^{-1}y^4)^3$

   A. $\dfrac{9y^{12}}{x^3}$

   B. $\dfrac{27y^{12}}{x^3}$

   C. $9x^2y^7$

   D. $27x^2y^7$

7. Subtract: $(6a^2 - 9a + 10) - (4a^2 + a - 3)$

   A. $2a^2 - 10a + 13$

   B. $2a^2 - 10a + 7$

   C. $2a^2 - 8a + 13$

   D. $2a^2 - 8a + 7$

8. Simplify: $(^-x + 6)(4x + 10)$

   A. $^-4x^2 + 60$

   B. $^-4x^2 + 34x + 60$

   C. $^-4x^2 + 14x + 60$

   D. $^-4x^2 - 10x + 60$

9. Mariah has driven 100 miles today. If she drives at a speed of 50 miles per hour for the next h hours, how far will she have driven in total today?

   A. $100 + 50 + h$

   B. $(100 + 50) \div h$

   C. $h(100 + 50)$

   D. $100 + 50h$

10. What is this quotient?

$$x + 2\,\overline{)4x^2 + 7x - 2}\,, x \neq\, ^-2$$

   A. $4x - 5$

   B. $4x - 1$

   C. $4x + 1$

   D. $4x + 5$

11. Simplify: $\sqrt[3]{^-24}$

   A. $^-3\sqrt[3]{4}$

   B. $^-3\sqrt[3]{2}$

   C. $^-2\sqrt[3]{6}$

   D. $^-2\sqrt[3]{3}$

12. Which of the following is a prime polynomial?

   A. $x^2 - 5x + 14$

   B. $2x^2 - 98$

   C. $3x^2 - 2x - 8$

   D. $9x^2 + 36x$

13. The phrase below describes an algebraic expression.

the square root of the product of a number x raised to the sixth power and a number y cubed

   A. Write the algebraic expression represented by this phrase.

   _____

   B. Simplify this algebraic expression.

   _____

   C. Evaluate the simplified expression for $x = 2$ and $y = 4$. Show your work.

Chapter 2   Equations and Inequalities

SOL: A.4.b, A.4.d

Solve One-Variable Linear Equations Algebraically

A **linear equation** is an equation in which the variable or variables are raised to the first power. A solution to an equation is the value or set of values that can be substituted to make the equation true. Solving a linear equation in one variable means finding the value of the variable that makes the equation true.

When solving linear equations, you should know some properties of equality. Note that these properties are valid only for the set of real numbers and its subsets.

For all real numbers a, b, and c:

Symmetric Property of Equality: If $a = b$, then $b = a$.

Transitive Property of Equality: If $a = b$ and $b = c$, then $a = c$.

Substitution Property of Equality: If $a = b$, then a can be substituted for b in any equation or inequality.

The substitution property of equality allows you to substitute an expression or value for an equivalent expression within an equation. Also, four specific properties of equality are subsets of the substitution property:

Addition Property of Equality: If $a = b$, then $a + c = b + c$ and $c + a = c + b$.

Subtraction Property of Equality: If $a = b$, then $a - c = b - c$.

Multiplication Property of Equality: If $a = b$, then $ac = bc$ and $ca = cb$.

Division Property of Equality: If $a = b$ and $c \neq 0$, then $a \div c = b \div c$.

In order to solve a linear equation, you must isolate the variable on one side of the equation.

To Solve a Linear Equation

- First use the addition property of equality and the subtraction property of equality as needed to move the terms containing variables to one side of the equation and to move all of the other terms to the other side of the equation. Combine any like terms.

- Next use the multiplication property of equality and the division property of equality as needed to isolate the variable.

- The solution is the resulting value of the variable.

- Check the solution by substituting the value back into the original equation. If a true sentence results, the solution is correct.

Example 1

Solve: $\frac{3}{4}(8x - 12) = 3$

Strategy   **Isolate the variable.**

Step 1   Apply the distributive property.

$$\frac{3}{4}(8x - 12) = 3$$

$$\frac{3}{4} \cdot 8x - \frac{3}{4} \cdot 12 = 3$$

$$6x - 9 = 3$$

Step 2   Add 9 to both sides of the equation.

$$6x - 9 = 3$$

$$6x - 9 + 9 = 3 + 9$$

$$6x = 12$$

Step 3   Divide both sides by 6, the coefficient of the variable.

$$6x = 12$$

$$\frac{6x}{6} = \frac{12}{6}$$

$$x = 2$$

Step 4   Check the solution by substituting 2 for x in the original equation.

$$\frac{3}{4}(8x - 12) = 3$$

$$\frac{3}{4}(8 \cdot 2 - 12) \overset{?}{=} 3$$

$$\frac{3}{4}(16 - 12) \overset{?}{=} 3$$

$$\frac{3}{4}(4) \overset{?}{=} 3$$

$$3 = 3 \checkmark$$

Solution $x = 2$

Example 2

Solve: $^-3(x - 5) = 4x + 5$

Strategy   **Isolate the variable.**

Step 1   Apply the distributive property.

$$^-3(x - 5) = 4x + 5$$
$$^-3x + 15 = 4x + 5$$

Step 2   Move all the variable terms to one side of the equation.

Add $3x$ to both sides.

$$^-3x + 15 = 4x + 5$$
$$^-3x + 15 + 3x = 4x + 5 + 3x$$
$$15 = 7x + 5$$

Step 3   Subtract 5 from both sides to isolate the variable term.

$$15 = 7x + 5$$
$$15 - 5 = 7x + 5 - 5$$
$$10 = 7x$$

Step 4   Divide both sides of the equation by 7.

$$10 \div 7 = 7x \div 7$$
$$\frac{10}{7} = x$$

Step 5   Check the solution.

$$^-3(x - 5) = 4x + 5$$
$$^-3\left(\frac{10}{7} - 5\right) \stackrel{?}{=} 4\left(\frac{10}{7}\right) + 5$$
$$^-\frac{30}{7} + 15 \stackrel{?}{=} \frac{40}{7} + 5$$
$$^-\frac{30}{7} + \frac{105}{7} \stackrel{?}{=} \frac{40}{7} + \frac{35}{7}$$
$$\frac{75}{7} = \frac{75}{7} \checkmark$$

Solution $x = \dfrac{10}{7}$

Sometimes when you solve an equation, all of the variable terms are eliminated and a number sentence results. If the number sentence is true, the solution of the equation is all real numbers. In other words, the equation has infinitely many solutions. If the number sentence is false, the equation has no solution.

If the solution is the set of all real numbers, you may use set-builder notation to indicate this, as follows: $\{x : x \in \mathbb{R}\}$. This is read as "the set of all x such that x is an element of the set of real numbers."

Example 3

Solve: $\frac{2}{3}(6x + 3) = 4x + 3$

Strategy   **Isolate the variable.**

Step 1   Apply the distributive property.

$$\frac{2}{3}(6x + 3) = 4x + 3$$

$$4x + 2 = 4x + 3$$

Step 2   Move the variable terms to one side of the equation.

Subtract $4x$ from both sides.

$$4x + 2 = 4x + 3$$

$$4x + 2 - 4x = 4x + 3 - 4x$$

$$2 = 3$$

Step 3   Look at the resulting number sentence.

All of the variable terms were eliminated.

$2 = 3$ is not a true statement, so this equation has no solution.

Solution   **There is no solution.**

Example 4

Solve: $0.7n - 2(0.4n + 8) = {}^-0.1n - 16$

Strategy   **Isolate the variable.**

Step 1   Apply the distributive property.

$$0.7n - 2(0.4n + 8) = {}^-0.1n - 16$$

$$0.7n - 0.8n - 16 = {}^-0.1n - 16$$

Add like terms.

$${}^-0.1n - 16 = {}^-0.1n - 16$$

Step 2   Move the variable terms to one side of the equation.

Add $0.1n$ to both sides.

$${}^-0.1n - 16 = {}^-0.1n - 16$$

$${}^-0.1n - 16 + 0.1n = {}^-0.1n - 16 + 0.1n$$

$${}^-16 = {}^-16$$

Step 3   Look at the resulting number sentence.

${}^-16 = {}^-16$ is a true sentence.

Solution   **The solution is all real numbers, or $\{x : x \in \mathbb{R}\}$.**

Coached Example

Solve: 2(⁻3x + 1) = 4(x + 3)

Apply the distributive property to both sides of the equation.

The result is _____ = _____.

Move the variable terms to one side of the equation.

Eliminate the variable term from the left side of the equation by adding _____ to both sides of the equation.

The result is _____ = _____.

Isolate the term containing the variable by subtracting _____ from both sides of the equation.

The result is _____ = _____.

Isolate the variable by dividing both sides of the equation by _____.

The result is x = _____.

Check your answer.

The solution is _____.

Lesson Practice

Choose the correct answer.

1. Solve: $10 = \frac{2}{5}x + 4$

   A. $x = \frac{12}{5}$

   B. $x = 15$

   C. $x = 21$

   D. $x = 35$

2. Solve: $5a - 8 = a + 8$

   A. $a = 0$

   B. $a = \frac{8}{3}$

   C. $a = 4$

   D. There is no solution.

3. Solve: $0.2(4x + 3) = 2.2$

   A. $x = {}^-1$

   B. $x = {}^-\frac{1}{4}$

   C. $x = \frac{11}{7}$

   D. $x = 2$

4. Solve: $^-3(2x - 1) = 9x + 3$

   A. $x = 0$

   B. $x = \frac{2}{5}$

   C. $\{x : x \in \mathbb{R}\}$

   D. There is no solution.

5. Solve: $2(3b - 4) = 4(b + 1) + 2b$

   A. $b = {}^-1$

   B. $b = 1$

   C. $\{b : b \in \mathbb{R}\}$

   D. There is no solution.

6. Solve: $\frac{5}{6}(4x + 6) = \frac{1}{3}x - 4$

   A. $x = {}^-3$

   B. $x = {}^-\frac{1}{2}$

   C. $x = \frac{1}{3}$

   D. $x = \frac{10}{3}$

7. Solve: $8x + 21 - x = 7(x + 3)$

   A. $x = 0$

   B. $x = 1$

   C. $\{x : x \in \mathbb{R}\}$

   D. There is no solution.

8. Solve: $\frac{3}{4}n + 3\left(\frac{1}{2}n - 1\right) = 2n - 1$

   A. $n = {}^-1$

   B. $n = 0$

   C. $n = 8$

   D. $n = 12$

Solve Literal Equations

SOL: A.4.a

A **literal equation** has more than one variable. Sometimes you need to solve a literal equation for one of the variables. To do this, use the properties of equality to isolate the variable you are solving for and treat the other variables like constants.

Example 1

Solve for c:

$$ax = 2b - cy$$

Strategy   Use the properties of equality to isolate c.

$$ax = 2b - cy$$

$ax - 2b = 2b - cy - 2b$ Subtract $2b$ from both sides.

$ax - 2b = {}^-cy$ Simplify.

$\dfrac{ax - 2b}{{}^-y} = \dfrac{{}^-cy}{{}^-y}$ Divide both sides by ${}^-y$.

$\dfrac{ax - 2b}{{}^-y} = c$

Solution $c = \dfrac{ax - 2b}{{}^-y}$

Example 2

Solve for l:

$$P = 3l - 2w$$

Strategy   Use the properties of equality to isolate l.

$$P = 3l - 2w$$

$P + 2w = 3l - 2w + 2w$ Add $2w$ to both sides.

$P + 2w = 3l$ Simplify.

$\dfrac{P + 2w}{3} = \dfrac{3l}{3}$ Divide both sides by 3.

$\dfrac{P + 2w}{3} = l$

Solution $l = \dfrac{P + 2w}{3}$

A **formula** is a literal equation that represents a general relationship among quantities. Mathematical formulas are used to express many geometric relationships, for example.

Example 3

The formula for finding the volume of a cone is: $V = \frac{1}{3}\pi r^2 h$. Solve for h.

Strategy   Use the properties of equality to isolate h.

$$V = \frac{1}{3}\pi r^2 h$$

$$3 \cdot V = 3 \cdot \frac{1}{3}\pi r^2 h \qquad \text{Multiply both sides by 3.}$$

$$3V = (1)\pi r^2 h \qquad \text{Simplify.}$$

$$3V = \pi r^2 h$$

$$\frac{3V}{\pi r^2} = \frac{\pi r^2 h}{\pi r^2} \qquad \text{Divide both sides by } \pi r^2.$$

$$\frac{3V}{\pi r^2} = h$$

Solution $h = \frac{3V}{\pi r^2}$

Coached Example

Solve $ax - ab = c + d$ for a.

The variable you must isolate is _____.

First use the _____ property to factor out this variable from the terms on the left side of the equation.

_____(_____ − _____) = $c + d$

Next you must _____ both sides of the equation by the entire expression (_____) to solve for a.

$a =$ _____

Lesson Practice

Choose the correct answer.

1. Solve for r:

   $$d = rt$$

   A. $r = dt$

   B. $r = \frac{d}{t}$

   C. $r = d - t$

   D. $r = d + t$

2. The formula for finding the area of a triangle is $A = \frac{1}{2}bh$, where b represents the base and h represents the height. Which equation can you use to find the base length, b, of the triangle?

   A. $b = 2Ah$

   B. $b = \frac{2h}{A}$

   C. $b = \frac{Ah}{2}$

   D. $b = \frac{2A}{h}$

3. Solve for w:

   $$P = 2l + 2w$$

   A. $w = P - 2l - 2$

   B. $w = \frac{P}{2} - 2l$

   C. $w = \frac{P - 2l}{2}$

   D. $w = 2P - l$

4. The formula for finding the volume of a square pyramid is $V = \frac{1}{3}s^2h$, where s represents the side length of the square base and h represents the height. Which equation can you use to find the height, h, of the square pyramid?

   A. $h = 3Vs^2$

   B. $h = \frac{3V}{s^2}$

   C. $h = \sqrt{3Vs}$

   D. $h = \sqrt{\frac{3V}{s}}$

5. Solve for s:

   $$A = 6s^2$$

   A. $s = \sqrt{A} - 6$

   B. $s = \sqrt{A - 6}$

   C. $s = \frac{\sqrt{A}}{6}$

   D. $s = \sqrt{\frac{A}{6}}$

6. The formula for converting from degrees Celsius, C, to degrees Fahrenheit, F, is $F = \frac{9}{5}C + 32$. Which formula converts from degrees Fahrenheit, F, to degrees Celsius, C?

   A. $C = \frac{9}{5}F - 32$

   B. $C = \frac{5}{9}(F - 32)$

   C. $C = \frac{5}{9}(F + 32)$

   D. $C = \frac{9}{5}(F - 32)$

Solve One-Variable Linear Equations Graphically

SOL: A.4.d

Consider a one-variable linear equation, such as $3x = x - 2$. Solving this equation means that you find the value of x that makes this equation true.

One way to rewrite this problem is as an equation in the form $f(x) = g(x)$. In order to do this, you must set the expression on one side of the original equation equal to $f(x)$ and set the expression on the other side equal to $g(x)$. Then you can graph each of those **functions** to find the value of x.

Example 1

Solve for x by graphing: $3x = x - 2$

Strategy   **Rewrite the equation as two equivalent functions and solve by graphing.**

Step 1   Rewrite $3x = x - 2$ as two equivalent functions.

Set the expression on the left side equal to $f(x)$: $f(x) = 3x$.

Set the expression on the right side equal to $g(x)$: $g(x) = x - 2$.

Step 2   Make a table of values for each function.

Both equations are linear, so you need to find only two points for each.

x	f(x) = 3x	f(x)
0	$f(x) = 3(0) = 0$	0
2	$f(x) = 3(2) = 6$	6

x	g(x) = x − 2	g(x)
0	$g(x) = 0 - 2 = -2$	-2
2	$g(x) = 2 - 2 = 0$	0

Step 3   Graph the functions.

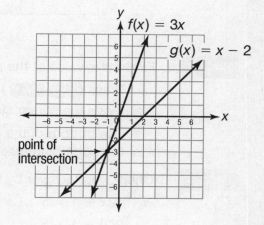

The value of x at the point where the two lines intersect is -1, so $x = -1$.

When $x = -1$, $f(x) = g(x)$ is true. This also means that $x = -1$ in the original equation.

Step 4   Check your answer by substituting -1 for x in the original equation.

Just from looking at the graph, you cannot be certain that the point of intersection is at $x = -1$. It may be at $x = -1.01$ or at $x = -0.99$. So check your answer algebraically.

$$3x = x - 2$$
$$3(-1) \overset{?}{=} (-1) - 2$$
$$-3 = -3, \text{ so } x = -1 \text{ makes the equation true.}$$

Solution   **The graph in Step 3 shows that the value of x is −1.**

You may also use a graphing calculator to graph the two functions and find the point of intersection. The keys to press on your calculator may be slightly different from the ones shown.

Example 2

Solve for x by graphing: $2x + 1 = 5$

Strategy   **Rewrite the equation as two equivalent functions and solve by graphing.**

Step 1   Rewrite $2x + 1 = 5$ as two equivalent functions.

Set the expression on the left side equal to $f(x)$: $f(x) = 2x + 1$.

Set the expression on the right side equal to $g(x)$: $g(x) = 5$.

Step 2   Use a graphing calculator to graph both functions.

Press Y= . Enter the first equation into Y_1, enter the second equation into Y_2, and hit GRAPH.

```
Y₁=2X+1
Y₂=5
```

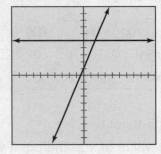

Step 3   Find the x-value at the point of intersection.

Press 2nd TRACE to access the CALC menu and select 5: INTERSECT. Move the cursor close to the intersection, then hit ENTER three times.

The bottom of the screen should show X = 2 and Y = 5. The value of x at the point of intersection is 2.

Step 4   Check your answer by substituting 2 for x in the original equation.

$$2x + 1 = 5$$
$$2(2) + 1 \overset{?}{=} 5$$
$$5 = 5, \text{ so } x = 2 \text{ makes the equation true.}$$

Solution   **The graphing calculator shows that the value of x is 2.**

Coached Example

Solve for _x_ by graphing: $\frac{1}{2}x = 9 - x$.

Set the expression on the left side equal to _f(x)_: _f(x)_ = _____.

Set the expression on the right side equal to _g(x)_: _g(x)_ = _____.

Complete the tables of values for _f(x)_ and _g(x)_.

x	f(x) = _____	f(x)
0		
2		

x	g(x) = _____	g(x)
0		
2		

Now use those points to graph and label the functions on the grid below.

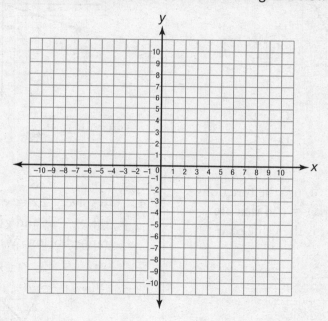

The value of _x_ at the point of intersection is _____, so _x_ = _____.

Check your answer by substituting that value of _x_ into the original equation.

$\frac{1}{2}x = 9 - x$

_____

_____

The graph shows that the value of _x_ that makes the equation $\frac{1}{2}x = 9 - x$ true is _____.

Choose the correct answer.

1. To solve $x - 3 = 2x - 5$, use the functions $f(x) = x - 3$ and $g(x) = 2x - 5$ that are graphed below. What is the value of x?

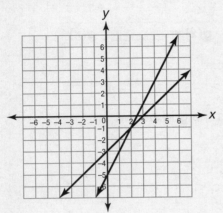

   A. $^-3$ C. 2
   B. $^-1$ D. 3

2. To solve $2x + 6 = {}^-4$, use the functions $f(x) = 2x + 6$ and $g(x) = {}^-4$ that are graphed below. What is the value of x?

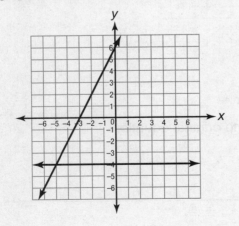

   A. $^-6$ C. $^-4$
   B. $^-5$ D. $^-3$

3. To solve $\frac{1}{3}x = {}^-x + 4$, use the functions $f(x) = \frac{1}{3}x$ and $g(x) = {}^-x + 4$ that are graphed below. What is the value of x?

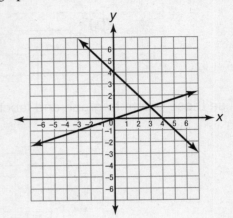

   A. 1   C. 3
   B. 2   D. 4

4. To solve $^-2x = x + 6$, use the functions $f(x) = {}^-2x$ and $g(x) = x + 6$ that are graphed below. What is the value of x?

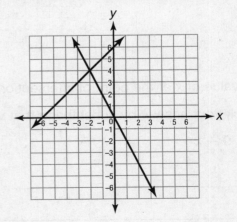

   A. $^-2$ C. 2
   B. $^-1$ D. 4

5. Use graphing to solve the equation
$x - 5 = ^-2$. What is the value of x?

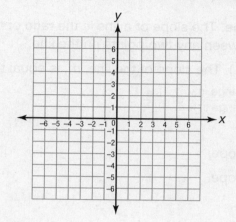

   A. $^-7$

   B. $^-5$

   C. $^-2$

   D. 3

6. Use graphing to solve the equation
$2x - 1 = x + 1$. What is the value of x?

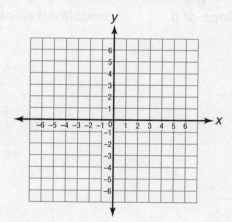

   A. 0

   B. 1

   C. 2

   D. 3

7. Use graphing to solve the equation
$^-2x - 6 = ^-x - 2$. What is the value of x?

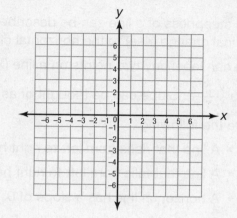

   A. $^-4$

   B. $^-2$

   C. 2

   D. 4

8. Use graphing to solve the equation
$\frac{1}{2}x - 2 = x - 1$. What is the value of x?

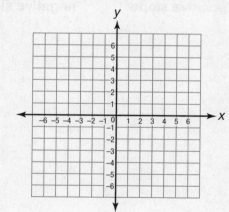

   A. $^-3$

   B. $^-2$

   C. $^-1$

   D. 1

Slope and Intercepts

SOL: A.6.a

The steepness of a line can be described using its **slope**. The slope of a line is the ratio of the vertical change (rise) to the horizontal change (run) between any two points on the line.

You can label any two points on a line (x_1, y_1) and (x_2, y_2). The slope of the line, m, is equal to the ratio $\frac{y_2 - y_1}{x_2 - x_1}$. Slope can be thought of as the fraction $\frac{\text{change in } y}{\text{change in } x}$ or $\frac{\text{rise}}{\text{run}}$.

Note the following:

- A line that rises from left to right has a positive slope.

- A line that falls from left to right has a negative slope.

- A horizontal line has a slope of 0.

- A vertical line has an undefined slope because the change in x for any vertical line is 0. Remember that a fraction with a denominator of 0 is undefined.

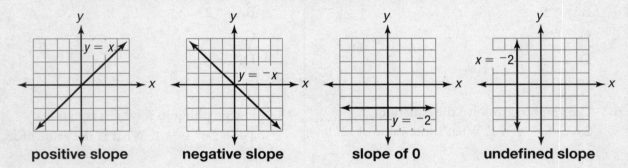

positive slope   negative slope   slope of 0   undefined slope

Example 1

What is the slope of the line in this graph?

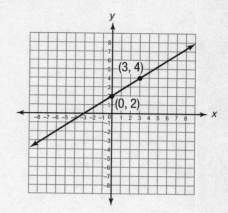

Strategy   **Choose two points on the line.**
Use them to find the slope.

Step 1   Pick any two points on the line.

Use (0, 2) and (3, 4).

Let (0, 2) be (x_1, y_1) and let (3, 4) be (x_2, y_2).

Step 2   Find the change in y.

$$y_2 - y_1 = 4 - 2 = 2$$

Step 3   Find the change in x.

$$x_2 - x_1 = 3 - 0 = 3$$

Step 4   Find the slope by writing the ratio $\frac{\text{change in } y}{\text{change in } x}$.

$$m = \frac{2}{3}$$

Solution   **The slope of the line is $\frac{2}{3}$.**

Example 2

Describe the slope of the line shown below as positive, negative, zero, or undefined.

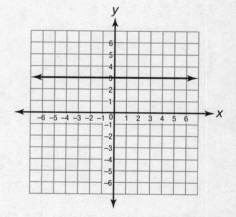

Strategy   **Examine the direction of the line.**

Step 1   Examine the direction of the line.

The line does not rise or fall from left to right. It is a horizontal line, so it has a slope of 0.

Step 2   Use two points to calculate the slope to confirm your answer.

Choose two points on the line.

Let (0, 3) be (x_1, y_1) and let (2, 3) be (x_2, y_2).

$$m = \frac{y_2 - y_1}{x_2 - x_1}$$

$$m = \frac{3 - 3}{2 - 0} = \frac{0}{2} = 0$$

Solution   **The line has a slope of 0.**

Parallel lines never intersect. A pair of parallel lines is shown below.

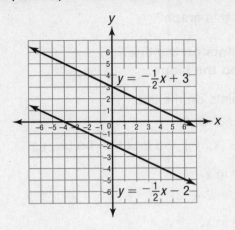

The lines in this graph are $y = -\frac{1}{2}x + 3$ and $y = -\frac{1}{2}x - 2$, which both have a slope of $-\frac{1}{2}$. Parallel lines always have the same slope, and any two lines that have the same slope must be parallel. Notice also that when $x = 0$, the y-values 3 and $^-2$ are exactly 5 units apart. For any x-value, the y-values of these two lines are exactly 5 units apart.

Perpendicular lines intersect at right angles. For example, the perpendicular lines $y = 3x - 2$ and $y = -\frac{1}{3}x + 2$ are shown below.

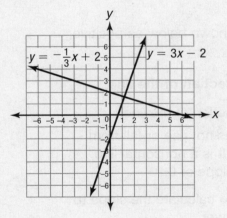

For all perpendicular lines, the slope of one line is the negative reciprocal of the slope of the other line. The slopes of the lines above, 3 and $-\frac{1}{3}$, are negative reciprocals of one another. $\left(\text{Remember, } 3 = \frac{3}{1}.\right)$ The product of the slopes of perpendicular lines is always $^-1$ unless one of the lines has an undefined slope.

Example 3

Given points $A(5, -3)$ and $B(-5, 5)$, find the slope of a line perpendicular to $\overleftrightarrow{AB}$.

Strategy **Find the slope of $\overleftrightarrow{AB}$, and then find its negative reciprocal.**

Step 1 Find the slope of $\overleftrightarrow{AB}$.

Use the slope equation, $m = \dfrac{y_2 - y_1}{x_2 - x_1}$.

$m = \dfrac{5 - (-3)}{-5 - 5} = \dfrac{8}{-10} = \dfrac{4}{-5} = -\dfrac{4}{5}$

Step 2 Find the negative reciprocal of this slope.

The negative reciprocal of $-\dfrac{4}{5}$ is $-\left(-\dfrac{5}{4}\right)$, or $\dfrac{5}{4}$.

Solution **The slope of a line perpendicular to $\overleftrightarrow{AB}$ is $\dfrac{5}{4}$.**

The **x-intercept** of a line is the point where the line intersects the x-axis. The ordered pair for a point that is an x-intercept always has a y-value of 0.

The **y-intercept** of a line is the point where the line intersects the y-axis. The ordered pair for a point that is a y-intercept always has an x-value of 0.

Coached Example

Write the ordered pairs for the x- and y-intercepts of the line in the graph below.

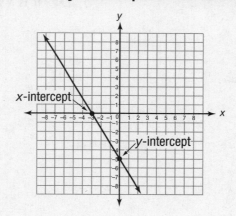

The x-intercept is the point where the line intersects the _____-axis.

The line crosses the x-axis at _____. The ordered pair for this point is (_____, 0).

The y-intercept is the point where the line intersects the _____-axis.

The line crosses the y-axis at _____. The ordered pair for this point is (0, _____).

The ordered pair for the x-intercept is (_____, _____); the ordered pair for the y-intercept is (_____, _____).

Lesson Practice

Choose the correct answer.

Use the graph below for questions 1–3.

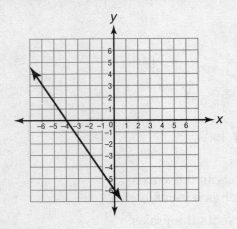

1. What is the *x*-intercept of this line?

    A. $^-6$

    B. $^-4$

    C. 4

    D. 6

2. What is the slope of this line?

    A. $-\dfrac{3}{2}$

    B. $-\dfrac{2}{3}$

    C. $\dfrac{2}{3}$

    D. $\dfrac{3}{2}$

3. What is the slope of a line perpendicular to this line?

    A. $-\dfrac{3}{2}$

    B. $-\dfrac{2}{3}$

    C. $\dfrac{2}{3}$

    D. $\dfrac{3}{2}$

4. Which of the following describes a line with a positive slope?

    A. It rises from left to right.

    B. It falls from left to right.

    C. It is a horizontal line.

    D. It is a vertical line.

5. A line is graphed below.

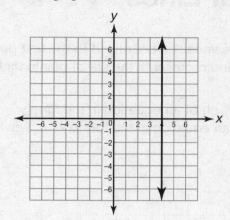

Which of the following describes the slope of this line?

A. positive

B. negative

C. zero

D. undefined

6. What is the slope of a line that passes through the points $(-2, 4)$ and $(7, 1)$?

A. -3

B. $-\dfrac{5}{3}$

C. $-\dfrac{3}{5}$

D. $-\dfrac{1}{3}$

7. A line is graphed below.

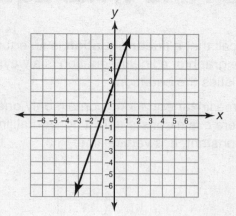

Which ordered pair represents the *y*-intercept of this line?

A. $(-1, 0)$

B. $(0, -1)$

C. $(0, 3)$

D. $(3, 0)$

8. Given points $Q(3, -2)$ and $R(-3, -8)$, what is the slope of a line parallel to $\overleftrightarrow{QR}$?

A. $-\dfrac{5}{3}$

B. -1

C. $\dfrac{3}{5}$

D. 1

Graph and Write Equations of Lines

SOL: A.6.a, A.6.b, A.7.f

Recall that a **linear equation** is an equation in which the variables are raised to the first power. The graph of a linear equation is always a straight line and represents the set of points that satisfies the equation.

Some linear equations contain only one variable. The graph of an equation in the form $y = c$, where c is a constant, is a horizontal line. The graph of an equation in the form $x = c$, where c is a constant, is a vertical line.

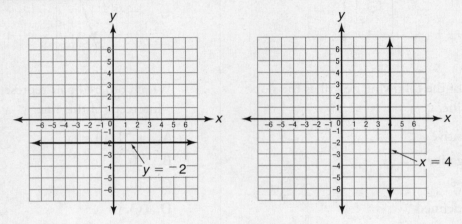

Many linear equations include two variables: x and y. The equation of a line in two variables defines the relationship between the two variables. You can graph a line if given any of the following information:

- Two points on the line
- The x- and y-intercepts of the line
- One point and the slope of the line
- The x- or y-intercept and the slope of the line
- The linear equation
- A table of values

If you are given one point and the slope of the line, graph the given point. Then use the slope to graph a second point and draw a line through the two points.

Example 1

Graph a line that has a slope of $-\frac{2}{3}$ and passes through the point $(-2, 4)$.

Strategy **Plot the given point, and use the slope to plot one additional point. Draw a line through the plotted points.**

Step 1 Plot the point $(-2, 4)$.

Step 2 Use the slope of $-\frac{2}{3}$ to find another point on the line.

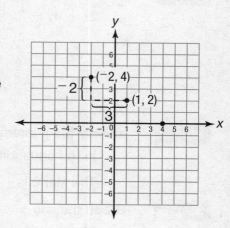

A negative slope means that the line falls from left to right. A slope of $-\frac{2}{3}$ is the same as $\frac{-2}{3}$, so the line falls 2 units for every 3 units it moves to the right. If you move down 2 units and to the right 3 units from $(-2, 4)$, you reach $(1, 2)$.

Plot a point at $(1, 2)$.

Step 3 Draw a line through the plotted points.

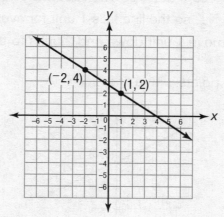

Solution **The line with a slope of $-\frac{2}{3}$ that passes through $(-2, 4)$ is graphed in Step 3.**

A line can be represented by its graph or by an equation. The **standard form of a linear equation** is $Ax + By = C$.

The **slope-intercept form of a linear equation** is written in the form $y = mx + b$. In this form, m represents the slope of the line and b represents the y-intercept. To graph a linear equation in slope-intercept form, plot the y-intercept point, use the slope to plot an additional point, and draw a line through the plotted points. If you are given a linear equation in any other form, solve for y so that the equation is in slope-intercept form. Then graph the line.

Example 2

Graph the line represented by the equation $2x + 4y = 12$.

Strategy   **Write the equation in slope-intercept form. Then use the slope and y-intercept to graph the line.**

Step 1   Solve for y to rewrite the equation in slope-intercept form.

$$2x + 4y - 2x = 12 - 2x \qquad \text{Subtract } 2x \text{ from both sides.}$$

$$4y = {}^-2x + 12$$

$$\frac{4y}{4} = \frac{-2x}{4} + \frac{12}{4} \qquad \text{Divide both sides by 4.}$$

$$y = {}^-\frac{1}{2}x + 3$$

Step 2   Identify the y-intercept (b) and slope (m).

In the equation $y = {}^-\frac{1}{2}x + 3$, $m = {}^-\frac{1}{2}$ and $b = 3$.

The slope is ${}^-\frac{1}{2}$, and the y-intercept is 3.

Step 3   Graph the line.

Plot the y-intercept at (0, 3). Then use the slope to find a second point.

The slope is ${}^-\frac{1}{2}$, so the line falls 1 unit for every 2 units it moves to the right.

From (0, 3), move 1 unit down and 2 units to the right. Plot the second point at (2, 2).

Connect the points with a line.

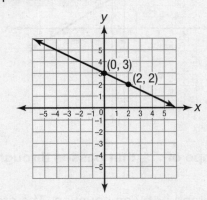

Solution   **The equation $2x + 4y = 12$ is graphed in Step 3.**

If you are given two points on a line, you can calculate the slope, determine the y-intercept, and write the equation in slope-intercept form. You can also use the statistics feature of a graphing calculator to find the equation of a line passing through two points.

Example 3

In slope-intercept form, what is the equation of the line passing through the points
($^-$1, $^-$8) and (3, 4)?

Strategy   **Find the slope and then the *y*-intercept. Write the equation in slope-intercept form. Then check your work using a graphing calculator.**

Step 1   Find the slope of the line.

$$m = \frac{y_2 - y_1}{x_2 - x_1}$$

$$m = \frac{4 - (^-8)}{3 - (^-1)}$$

$$m = \frac{12}{4} = 3$$

Step 2   Solve for the *y*-intercept.

Use the coordinates of one of the given points as *x* and *y*.

Use the point (3, 4). Substitute 3 for *x* and 4 for *y*.
Also substitute the slope, 3, for *m*.

$$y = mx + b$$
$$4 = 3(3) + b$$
$$4 = 9 + b$$
$$^-5 = b$$

The *y*-intercept is $^-$5.

Step 3   Write the equation of the line, using the slope and *y*-intercept.

$$y = mx + b$$
$$y = 3x - 5$$

Step 4   Enter the coordinates of the two points in your graphing calculator.

Enter the coordinates of the points into lists L₁ and L₂.

Hit **STAT** and then **ENTER** to access the lists. To clear out old data from a list, move the cursor up and highlight the list number, such as L1. Then press **CLEAR** and **ENTER**.

Be careful to keep the pairs of *x*- and *y*-coordinates on the same horizontal line.

L₁	L₂	L₃
−1	−8	-------
3	4	
-------	-------	

Step 5 Define the relationship as a linear equation for your calculator.

Press STAT then arrow to the right to select the CALC menu. Select number 4: LinReg(ax+b).

Step 6 Use the calculator to find the equation of the line.

On the home screen, enter the lists that contain your points. Type L_1, L_2, Y_1. To do this, press the 2nd key and 1, press the comma key, and then press the 2nd key and 2. Next press the comma key and the VARS key. Move the cursor to the right to highlight Y-VARS. Select 1: Function and then select 1: Y_1. The comma key is located above the 7 key.

Your screen should read "LinReg(ax+b) L_1, L_2, Y_1."

Press ENTER. On the resulting screen, "a" is the slope and "b" is the y-intercept.

Press Y= to see the equation of the line. Make sure that only line Y_1 has any information. If not, clear all other lines by pressing CLEAR.

Press GRAPH to see the graph of the line.

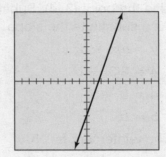

Plot1 Plot2 Plot3
$Y_1 = 3X + -5$
$Y_2 =$

Remember that addition of a negative number is the same as subtraction, so the equation is $y = 3x - 5$.

Solution **In slope-intercept form, the equation of the line passing through $(-1, -8)$ and $(3, 4)$ is $y = 3x - 5$.**

The **point-slope form of a linear equation** is written in the form $y - y_1 = m(x - x_1)$. This is called point-slope form because it uses a point on the line, (x_1, y_1), and the slope, m, to express the equation.

Note that if you are given two points on a line, you can calculate the slope and then use the coordinates of one of the points, along with the slope, in the point-slope form to find the equation of the line.

Example 4

What line is parallel to the line whose equation is $x - 3y = {}^-9$ and has an x-intercept of 12?

Strategy   **Find the slope of the line whose equation is $x - 3y = {}^-9$, and write the equation of the line that has the same slope and an x-intercept of 12.**

Step 1   Find the slope of the line $x - 3y = {}^-9$.

Solve the equation for y to put it in slope-intercept form.

$$x - 3y = {}^-9$$

$$-3y = {}^-x - 9$$

$$\frac{{}^-3y}{{}^-3} = \frac{{}^-x - 9}{{}^-3}$$

$$y = \frac{{}^-x}{{}^-3} + \frac{{}^-9}{{}^-3}$$

$$y = \frac{1}{3}x + 3$$

Identify the slope, m. The slope of this line is $\frac{1}{3}$.

Step 2   Write the equation of the parallel line using the slope $\frac{1}{3}$ and the x-intercept.

The x-intercept is 12, which is the point (12, 0).

Parallel lines have the same slope. So find the line with a slope of $\frac{1}{3}$ that passes through the point (12, 0). Use the point-slope form, $y - y_1 = m(x - x_1)$.

$$y - 0 = \frac{1}{3}(x - 12) \qquad \text{Simplify.}$$

$$y = \frac{1}{3}x - 4$$

Solution   The line whose equation is $y = \frac{1}{3}x - 4$ has an x-intercept of 12 and is parallel to the line $x - 3y = {}^-9$.

Coached Example

Graph the points shown in the table of values below, and write the equation of the line.

x	−1	0	1	2
y	−5	−2	1	4

Each pair of values (x, y) represents a point on the line.

Four points on the line are (_____, _____), (_____, _____), (_____, _____), and (_____, _____).

Plot these points on the coordinate grid below, and connect them with a straight line.

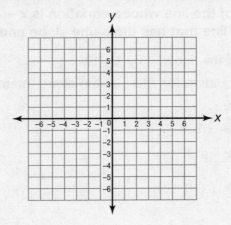

The slope of this line is _____.

The y-intercept of this line is _____.

Use the slope and y-intercept to write the equation of the line: _____

The equation of the line graphed above is _____.

Lesson Practice

Choose the correct answer.

1. Which of the following lines has an
   x-intercept of ⁻2 and a *y*-intercept of 2?

   A.

   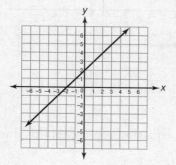

   B.

   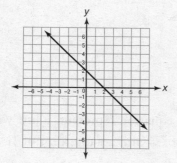

   C.

   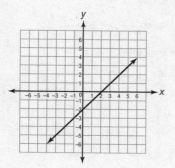

   D.

   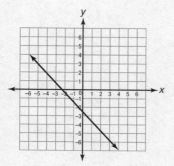

2. What is the slope of the line whose
   equation is $3x - 4y = 8$?

   A. $-\frac{4}{3}$

   B. $-\frac{3}{4}$

   C. $\frac{3}{4}$

   D. $\frac{4}{3}$

3. Which equation represents a line with
   a slope of 4 that passes through the
   point (2, 3)?

   A. $y = 4x - 11$

   B. $y = 4x - 5$

   C. $y = 4x + 1$

   D. $y = 4x + 3$

4. A line is graphed below.

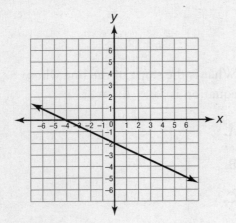

Which equation represents this line?

A. $y = -\frac{1}{2}x - 2$

B. $y = -2x - 2$

C. $y = \frac{1}{2}x - 2$

D. $y = 2x - \frac{1}{2}$

5. Which equation represents a line that passes through $(2, {}^-1)$ and $(6, 7)$?

A. $y = \frac{3}{2}x - 2$

B. $y = \frac{3}{2}x - 4$

C. $y = 2x - 3$

D. $y = 2x - 5$

6. A line is graphed below.

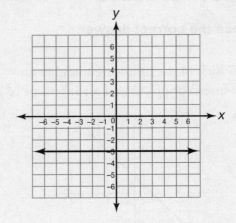

Which equation represents this line?

A. $x = {}^-3$

B. $y = {}^-3$

C. $y = x - 3$

D. $y = {}^-3x$

7. Which equation represents a line with a slope of ${}^-\frac{3}{2}$ and a y-intercept of 1?

A. $2x - 3y = 2$

B. $2x + 3y = 1$

C. $3x - 2y = 1$

D. $3x + 2y = 2$

Changes to the Slope and *y*-Intercept

SOL: A.6.a, A.6.b

When you change the values of *m* and/or *b* in the slope-intercept form of an equation, $y = mx + b$, the graph of the equation changes in certain ways.

- If the slope, *m*, is positive and you increase its value, the line becomes steeper.
- If the slope, *m*, is positive and you decrease its positive value (that is, the value gets closer to 0), the line becomes less steep.
- If the slope, *m*, is negative and you decrease its value, the line becomes steeper.
- If the slope, *m*, is negative and you increase its negative value (that is, the negative value gets closer to 0), the line becomes less steep.
- If the *y*-intercept, *b*, increases, the line shifts upward and is parallel to the original line.
- If the *y*-intercept, *b*, decreases, the line shifts downward and is parallel to the original line.

A change to the slope is considered a **dilation of a line** because it affects the steepness of the line. A shift of a line vertically without changing its slope is called a **translation of a line**.

You can compare the graph of a linear equation to the graph of the parent function $y = x$ by graphing both equations on the same coordinate plane.

Example 1

What happens to the graph of $y = x$ if the slope of the line is doubled?

Strategy   **Graph the parent function $y = x$. Then multiply the slope by 2 and graph the new equation on the same coordinate plane. Compare the graphs.**

Step 1   Graph $y = x$.

        The slope is 1 or $\frac{1}{1}$.

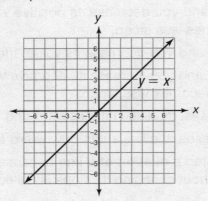

Step 2   Write the equation of the line whose slope is twice the slope of the parent function, and graph it.

        The slope of the graph of the parent function is 1. So the slope of the new line is $2 \cdot 1$, or 2.

        Graph the equation $y = 2x$ on the same coordinate plane.

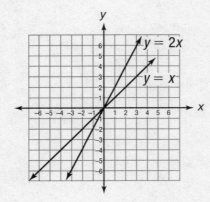

Step 3   Compare the graphs.

        Since the slope of the original equation is positive and doubling its value increases the slope, the line became steeper.

Solution   **When the slope of the line with equation $y = x$ is doubled, the line becomes steeper.**

Example 2

What happens to the graph of $y = -\frac{1}{2}x + 3$ if the value of the *y*-intercept decreases by 5 units?

Strategy   **Graph $y = -\frac{1}{2}x + 3$. Then decrease the *y*-intercept by 5 and graph the new equation on the same coordinate plane. Compare the graphs.**

Step 1   Graph $y = -\frac{1}{2}x + 3$.

The slope is $-\frac{1}{2}$ and the *y*-intercept is 3.

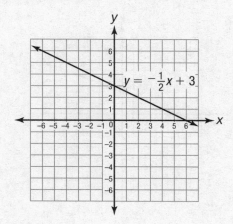

Step 2   Write the equation of the line whose *y*-intercept is 5 units less and graph the line.

The *y*-intercept of the original line is 3, so the *y*-intercept of the new line is $3 - 5$, or $^-2$.

Graph the equation $y = -\frac{1}{2}x - 2$ on the same coordinate plane.

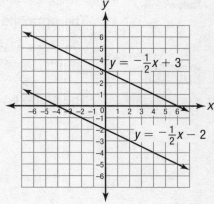

Step 3   Compare the graphs.

Since the value of the *y*-intercept decreased by 5 units, the graph of the equation shifted down 5 units. The graph of $y = -\frac{1}{2}x - 2$ is parallel to the original line.

Solution   **If the value of the *y*-intercept in the equation $y = -\frac{1}{2}x + 3$ decreases by 5, the line translates down 5 units and is parallel to the original line.**

Example 3

What happens to the graph of $y = \frac{2}{5}x + 2$ if the slope is replaced by its opposite?

Strategy   **Graph $y = \frac{2}{5}x + 2$. Then replace the slope in this equation with its opposite. Graph the new equation on the same coordinate plane and compare.**

Step 1   Graph $y = \frac{2}{5}x + 2$.

        The slope is $\frac{2}{5}$ and the y-intercept is 2.

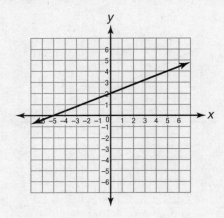

Step 2   Write the equation of the line with the opposite slope and same y-intercept.

        The opposite of $\frac{2}{5}$ is $-\frac{2}{5}$.

$$y = -\frac{2}{5}x + 2$$

Step 3   Graph $y = -\frac{2}{5}x + 2$ on the same coordinate plane.

        The slope is $-\frac{2}{5}$ and the y-intercept is 2.

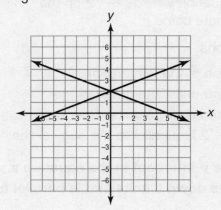

Step 4   Use a graphing calculator to check your work.

        Press [Y=]. Enter the first equation, $y = \frac{2}{5}x + 2$, into Y_1.

        Enter the second equation, $y = -\frac{2}{5}x + 2$, into Y_2.

        Hit [GRAPH]. The graph on the screen should look like the graph shown in Step 3.

Step 5   Compare the graphs.

The two graphs are reflections of one another across the vertical *y*-axis.

Solution   Replacing the slope of $y = \frac{2}{5}x + 2$ with its opposite results in a reflection of the line across the *y*-axis.

Coached Example

The graph of the equation $y = 3x + 1$ is shown below.

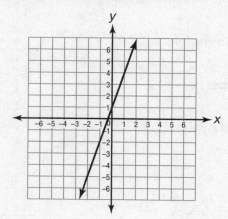

If the slope of $y = 3x + 1$ is decreased by 2, how will the graph of the new equation compare with the graph of the original equation?

If the *y*-intercept of $y = 3x + 1$ is increased by 2, how will the graph of the new equation compare with the graph of the original equation?

When the slope is decreased but remains positive, does a line become steeper or less steep?

_____

If the slope of $y = 3x + 1$ is decreased by 2, the line becomes _____.

When the *y*-intercept is increased, does the line shift upward or downward? _____

If the *y*-intercept of $y = 3x + 1$ is increased by 2, the line is translated _____ by ____ units.

If the slope of $y = 3x + 1$ is decreased by 2, the line becomes

_____.

If the *y*-intercept of $y = 3x + 1$ is increased by 2, the line is translated

_____.

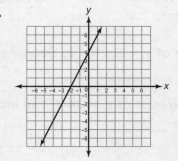
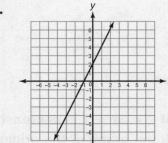
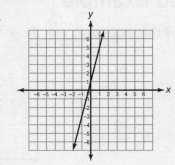
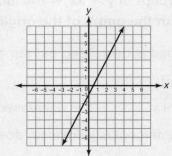

Lesson Practice

Choose the correct answer.

1. In the parent graph, $y = x$, how does multiplying x by a constant, a, affect the graph?

    A. The graph is translated upward or downward.

    B. The graph is translated to the left or to the right.

    C. The graph becomes steeper or less steep.

    D. The graph is not affected by the multiplication of x by a.

2. How does the graph of $y = {}^-2x + 4$ compare with the graph of $y = {}^-2x$?

    A. It is parallel to the line $y = {}^-2x$ but 4 units lower.

    B. It is parallel to the line $y = {}^-2x$ but 4 units higher.

    C. It is steeper than the line $y = {}^-2x$.

    D. It is less steep than the line $y = {}^-2x$.

3. Which of the following equations represents a dilation of the line $y = 2x - 7$?

    A. $y = 2x$

    B. $y = 2x + 7$

    C. $y = 2x - 4$

    D. $y = x - 7$

4. Which graph shows the result of decreasing the y-intercept of $y = 2x + 1$ by 2?

    A.

    B.

    C.

    D.

5. Which equation represents a line that is half as steep as the parent graph $y = x$?

   A. $y = \frac{1}{2}x$

   B. $y = 2x$

   C. $y = x - \frac{1}{2}$

   D. $y = x + \frac{1}{2}$

6. Which equation represents a translation of the graph of $y = {}^-4x - 3$ upward by 2 units?

   A. $y = {}^-4x - 5$

   B. $y = {}^-4x - 1$

   C. $y = {}^-4x + 2$

   D. $y = {}^-2x - 3$

7. Which equation represents a reflection of the graph of $y = {}^-2x + 5$ across the *y*-axis?

   A. $y = {}^-2x - 5$

   B. $y = {}^-2x + 5$

   C. $y = 2x - 5$

   D. $y = 2x + 5$

8. Which graph shows the result of doubling the slope of $y = {}^-x + 3$?

   A.

   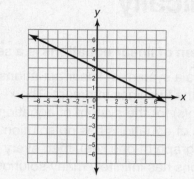

   B.

   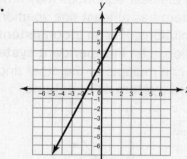

   C.

   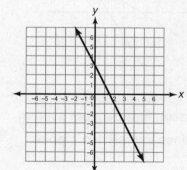

   D.

   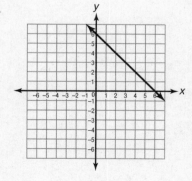

Solve Systems of Linear Equations Graphically

SOL: A.4.e

A **system of linear equations** is a set of two or more linear equations in the same variables.

To solve a system of linear equations graphically, graph each equation. Then identify any points where the two lines intersect. The *x*- and *y*-values of the point(s) of intersection represent the solution(s) for the system of equations. If the two lines are parallel and never intersect, the system of equations has no solution. If the two are **coincident lines** (the graphs will appear to be the graph of one line), then every point on the line is a solution. As a result, the system of equations has infinitely many solutions.

A system of linear equations may have one solution, no solution, or infinitely many solutions. If the system has at least one solution, it is a **consistent system of equations**. If the system has no solutions, it is an **inconsistent system of equations**. A consistent system with only one solution is an **independent system of equations**. A consistent system where one linear equation is a multiple of the other and, therefore, has an infinite number of solutions is a **dependent system of equations**.

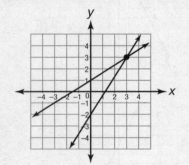

one solution;
consistent, independent system

The lines intersect in 1 point.

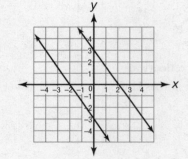

no solution;
inconsistent system

The lines are parallel.

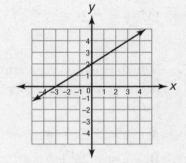

infinitely many solutions;
consistent, dependent system

The lines are coincident.

Example 1

Solve the system of linear equations graphically.

$$\begin{cases} 2x + y = 5 \\ y = \frac{1}{3}x - 2 \end{cases}$$

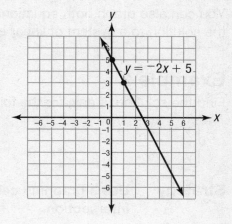

Strategy   **Graph each line, and identify the coordinates of their point of intersection.**

 Step 1   Graph $2x + y = 5$ on a coordinate grid.

Rewrite the equation in slope-intercept form by subtracting $2x$ from both sides.

$y = ^-2x + 5$

Plot the y-intercept at $(0, 5)$. The slope of $^-2$, or $\frac{^-2}{1}$, means move down 2 units and move right 1 unit. Plot the point. Then draw the line.

 Step 2   Graph $y = \frac{1}{3}x - 2$ on the same coordinate grid.

This line has a y-intercept of $^-2$. Plot a point at $(0, ^-2)$.

A slope of $\frac{1}{3}$ means move up 1 unit and move right 3 units. Plot the point. Then draw the line.

 Step 3   Identify the coordinates of the point of intersection.

The point where the two lines intersect is $(3, ^-1)$.

Both equations in the system are true only when $x = 3$ and $y = ^-1$.

Step 4   Check the solution.

Substitute $(3, ^-1)$ into each equation.

$$2x + y = 5 \qquad\qquad y = \frac{1}{3}x - 2$$
$$2(3) + (^-1) \stackrel{?}{=} 5 \qquad\qquad ^-1 \stackrel{?}{=} \frac{1}{3}(3) - 2$$
$$6 - 1 \stackrel{?}{=} 5 \qquad\qquad ^-1 \stackrel{?}{=} 1 - 2$$
$$5 = 5 \checkmark \qquad\qquad ^-1 = ^-1 \checkmark$$

Solution   **The solution for this system of linear equations is $(3, ^-1)$.**

You can also graph both equations and use the calc function on a graphing calculator to find the solution to a system of linear equations.

Example 2

Find the solution, if any, for the following system of linear equations.

$$\begin{cases} y = \frac{2}{3}x - 4 \\ y = {}^-x \end{cases}$$

Strategy   **Use a graphing calculator to graph both lines and find the point of intersection.**

Step 1   Graph both lines on a graphing calculator.

Press [Y=]. Enter the first equation, $y = \frac{2}{3}x - 4$, into Y_1.

Enter the second equation, $y = {}^-x$, into Y_2.

Press [GRAPH].

Step 2   Use the calc function to find the point of intersection.

Press [2nd] [TRACE] to access the CALC menu and choose number 5: intersect. Move the cursor close to the intersection of the two lines, and hit [ENTER] three times. The bottom of the screen should show X = 2.4 and Y = $^-$2.4, so the point of intersection is (2.4, $^-$2.4).

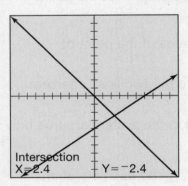

Intersection
X=2.4   Y=$^-$2.4

Solution   **The solution for this system of linear equations is (2.4, $^-$2.4).**

Coached Example

Graph $2y + x = 8$ and $3x + 6y = 0$ on the same coordinate plane. If the lines intersect, find the point of intersection.

Rewrite the equation $2y + x = 8$ in slope-intercept form: _____

This line has a slope of _____ and a y-intercept of _____.

Plot the y-intercept and use the slope to find a second point

Rewrite the equation $3x + 6y = 0$ in slope-intercept form: _____

This line has a slope of _____ and a y-intercept of _____.

Plot the y-intercept and use the slope to find a second point.

Graph both lines on the coordinate grid below.

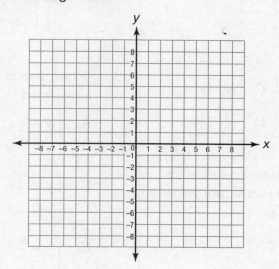

Do the lines intersect? _____

The two lines have the same _____, so they are _____.
The system of linear equations is an _____ system of equations,
so it has _____ solution.

Lesson Practice

Choose the correct answer.

1. Which is the solution for the system of linear equations shown below?

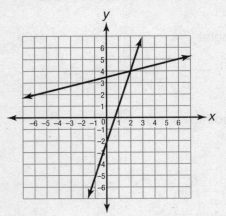

   A. $(0, {}^-2)$ **C.** $(2, 4)$

   B. $(1, 4)$ **D.** $\left(\frac{1}{2}, 3\frac{1}{2}\right)$

2. Which is the best approximate solution for the system of linear equations shown below?

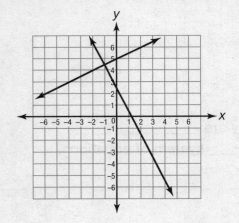

   A. $\left(-1\frac{1}{2}, 4\right)$ **C.** $\left(1, 4\frac{1}{2}\right)$

   B. $\left(-1, 4\frac{1}{2}\right)$ **D.** $\left(1\frac{1}{2}, 4\right)$

Use the graph below for questions 3 and 4.

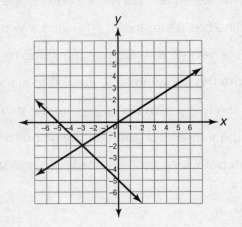

3. Which system of linear equations is represented by this graph?

   A. $\begin{cases} y = \frac{2}{3}x \\ y = {}^-x - 5 \end{cases}$

   B. $\begin{cases} y = \frac{2}{3}x \\ y = x - 5 \end{cases}$

   C. $\begin{cases} y = \frac{3}{2}x \\ y = {}^-x - 5 \end{cases}$

   D. $\begin{cases} y = \frac{3}{2}x \\ y = x - 5 \end{cases}$

4. What is the solution to this system of linear equations?

   A. $({}^-3, {}^-2)$

   B. $(0, 0)$

   C. $(0, 5)$

   D. $(3, {}^-2)$

5. Which of these graphs could be used to find the solution for the following system of linear equations?

$$\begin{cases} x + y = 4 \\ y = 2x - 5 \end{cases}$$

A.

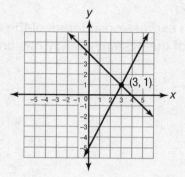

(3, 1)

B.

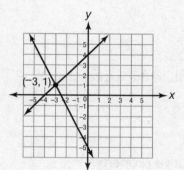

(−3, 1)

C.

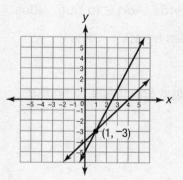

(1, −3)

D.

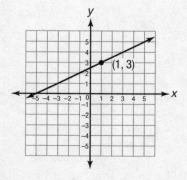

(1, 3)

6. Which best describes the graph of the following system of linear equations?

$$\begin{cases} y = -\frac{1}{2}x + 1 \\ 3x + 6y = -6 \end{cases}$$

A. The two lines coincide, so they are the same line.

B. The two lines intersect and are perpendicular.

C. The two lines intersect but are not perpendicular.

D. The two lines are parallel.

7. Which best describes the graph of a system of linear equations for which there are infinitely many solutions?

A. two parallel lines

B. two lines that intersect at exactly one point

C. two lines that intersect at exactly two points

D. two lines that coincide

Solve Systems of Linear Equations Algebraically

SOL: A.4.e

An algebraic strategy for solving a system of linear equations is to simplify the system by eliminating one of the variables.

In the substitution method, you replace one variable with an expression in terms of the other variable. This method is particularly helpful if one equation of the system already has one of the variables isolated on one side of the equation.

Example 1

Solve algebraically and check.

$$\begin{cases} y = 3x - 1 \\ 7x + 2y = 37 \end{cases}$$

Strategy   **Eliminate the variable y using substitution.**

Step 1   Since the first equation is solved for y, substitute the expression $3x - 1$ for y in the second equation. Solve for x.

$$7x + 2y = 37$$

$7x + 2(3x - 1) = 37$ Substitute for y.

$7x + 6x - 2 = 37$ Use the distributive property.

$13x = 39$ Combine like terms. Add 2 to both sides.

$\dfrac{13x}{13} = \dfrac{39}{13}$ Divide both sides by 13.

$x = 3$

Step 2   Substitute the value of x into one of the original equations to find y.

Use the first equation.

$y = 3x - 1$

$y = 3(3) - 1$ Substitute 3 for x.

$y = 9 - 1$ Simplify.

$y = 8$

Step 3 To check the solution, substitute 3 for *x* and 8 for *y* into both original equations.

$$y = 3x - 1 \qquad\qquad 7x + 2y = 37$$
$$8 \overset{?}{=} 3(3) - 1 \qquad\qquad 7(3) + 2(8) \overset{?}{=} 37$$
$$8 \overset{?}{=} 9 - 1 \qquad\qquad 21 + 16 \overset{?}{=} 37$$
$$8 = 8 \checkmark \qquad\qquad 37 = 37 \checkmark$$

(3, 8) makes both equations true.

Solution **The solution of the system of linear equations is (3, 8).**

Another way to solve a system of linear equations algebraically is to eliminate a variable using addition or subtraction. You may have to multiply one or both of the equations by a constant to make coefficients of like terms opposites.

Example 2

Solve algebraically and check.

$$\begin{cases} 3x - 4y = 26 \\ x + 2y = 2 \end{cases}$$

Strategy **Use multiplication to make the coefficients of one of the variables opposites.**

Step 1 Decide which variable to eliminate.

If you multiply the second equation by 2, the coefficients of *y* will be opposites (−4 and 4). You can then add the equations to eliminate *y*.

If you multiply the second equation by −3, the coefficients of *x* will be opposites (3 and −3). You can then add the equations to eliminate *x*.

Step 2 Multiply the second equation by 2.

$$2(x + 2y = 2) \rightarrow 2x + 4y = 4$$

Step 3 Add the result in Step 2 to the original first equation.

$$\begin{array}{r} 2x + 4y = 4 \\ + 3x - 4y = 26 \\ \hline 5x = 30 \end{array}$$

Step 4 Solve for *x*.

$$5x = 30$$
$$\frac{5x}{5} = \frac{30}{5} \qquad \text{Divide both sides by 5.}$$
$$x = 6$$

Step 5   Substitute $x = 6$ into an original equation that contains both variables to find y.

$$x + 2y = 2$$
$$6 + 2y = 2 \qquad \text{Substitute 6 for } x.$$
$$2y = {}^{-}4 \qquad \text{Subtract 6 from both sides.}$$
$$y = {}^{-}2 \qquad \text{Divide both sides by 2.}$$

Step 6   Check your solution in the original equations.

$3x - 4y = 26$	$x + 2y = 2$
$3(6) - 4({}^{-}2) \overset{?}{=} 26$	$6 + 2({}^{-}2) \overset{?}{=} 2$
$18 + 8 \overset{?}{=} 26$	$6 - 4 \overset{?}{=} 2$
$26 = 26$ ✓	$2 = 2$ ✓

Solution   **The solution of the system of linear equations is (6, $^{-}$2).**

Sometimes when you use addition or subtraction to solve a system of equations, both variables will be eliminated. If both variables are eliminated and you get a true equation, the system is a dependent system and has infinitely many solutions. If you get a false equation, the system is an inconsistent system and has no solution.

Example 3

Does this system have one solution, no solution, or infinitely many solutions?

$$\begin{cases} 5x + 3y = {}^{-}10 \\ {}^{-}5x - 3y = 10 \end{cases}$$

Strategy   **Solve the system using addition or subtraction.**

Step 1   Examine the coefficients of x and y in each equation.

The coefficients of x are opposites, and the coefficients of y are opposites.

Step 2   Add the equations.

$$\begin{array}{r} 5x + 3y = {}^{-}10 \\ + \ {}^{-}5x - 3y = 10 \\ \hline 0 = 0 \end{array}$$

Step 3   Examine the resulting sentence.

$0 = 0$ is a true sentence. The system is a dependent system of equations.

Solution   **The system of equations has infinitely many solutions.**

You can also solve a system of equations using a table of values.

Example 4

Solve using a table of values.

$$\begin{cases} 4x + y = 3 \\ {}^-x - 2y = 8 \end{cases}$$

Strategy   **Make a table of values for the two equations, using a graphing calculator. Find the solution they have in common.**

Step 1   Solve each equation for y to put each in slope-intercept form.

$$4x + y = 3 \qquad\qquad {}^-x - 2y = 8$$
$$y = {}^-4x + 3 \qquad\qquad {}^-2y = x + 8$$
$$\qquad\qquad\qquad\qquad y = {}^-\frac{1}{2}x - 4$$

Step 2   Use a graphing calculator to create a table of values for the two equations.

Press Y= . Enter the first equation, $y = {}^-4x + 3$, as Y_1, and enter the second equation, $y = {}^-\frac{1}{2}x - 4$, as Y_2.

Press 2nd GRAPH to access the TABLE feature. This brings up a table of values for the two equations, as shown below.

X	Y_1	Y_2
−3	15	−2.5
−2	11	−3
−1	7	−3.5
0	3	−4
1	−1	−4.5
2	−5	−5
3	−9	−5.5

Step 3   Identify the solution that the two equations have in common.

The only x-value in the table that has the same corresponding y-value ($^-5$) in both the Y_1 column and the Y_2 column is 2. The ordered pair $(2, {}^-5)$ is a solution to both $y = {}^-4x + 3$ and $y = {}^-\frac{1}{2}x - 4$.

Solution   **The solution of the system of linear equations is $(2, {}^-5)$.**

Coached Example

Solve by substitution and check.

$$\begin{cases} 4x + 3y = 27 \\ y = 1 - 2x \end{cases}$$

In the first equation, replace y with $1 - 2x$. _____

Solve for x.

$x =$ _____

Substitute your value for x into $y = 1 - 2x$. _____

Solve for y.

$y =$ _____

Check your values for x and y in both original equations.

The solution written as an ordered pair is (_____, _____).

Lesson Practice

Choose the correct answer.

1. Solve the system of linear equations:

$$\begin{cases} x = y + 2 \\ 2x + 4y = -2 \end{cases}$$

   A. $(0, -2)$ **C.** $(1, -1)$

   B. $(2, 0)$ **D.** $(-1, 1)$

2. Solve the system of linear equations:

$$\begin{cases} y = x + 7 \\ 2y - x = 10 \end{cases}$$

   A. $(-4, 3)$ **C.** $(-2, 5)$

   B. $(-3, 4)$ **D.** $(3, 10)$

3. Solve the system of linear equations:

$$\begin{cases} 2x + 6y = 12 \\ 2x - 2y = 4 \end{cases}$$

   A. $(0, 2)$ **C.** $(2, 0)$

   B. $(1, 3)$ **D.** $(3, 1)$

4. Solve the system of linear equations:

$$\begin{cases} 3x = y + 4 \\ x - y = 6 \end{cases}$$

   A. $(-7, -1)$ **C.** $(1, 7)$

   B. $(-1, -7)$ **D.** $(7, 1)$

5. Solve the system of linear equations:

$$\begin{cases} 3x - 9y = 12 \\ 3y = -x + 4 \end{cases}$$

   A. $(4, 0)$

   B. $\left(8, \dfrac{4}{3}\right)$

   C. There are no solutions.

   D. There are infinitely many solutions.

6. Solve the system of linear equations:

$$\begin{cases} 6y = 3x + 18 \\ x - 2y = 10 \end{cases}$$

   A. $(2, 4)$

   B. $(8, -1)$

   C. There are no solutions.

   D. There are infinitely many solutions.

7. Solve the system of linear equations:

$$\begin{cases} 8x + 4y = -12 \\ 3y = -6x - 9 \end{cases}$$

   A. $(-3, 3)$

   B. $(-1, -1)$

   C. There are no solutions.

   D. There are infinitely many solutions.

8. Which of the following best describes this system of linear equations?

$$\begin{cases} x - 2y = -7 \\ 4y = 2x + 28 \end{cases}$$

   A. consistent system of linear equations

   B. inconsistent system of linear equations

   C. dependent system of linear equations

   D. independent system of linear equations

Use Linear Equations to Solve Real-World Problems

SOL: A.4.f, A.7.f

Many real-world problems can be modeled and solved using linear equations or systems of linear equations.

> **Writing a Linear Equation to Model a Problem**
> 1. Read the problem carefully. Be sure you understand what it is asking.
> 2. Determine the variable. Write it down.
> 3. Figure out the relationship between the variable and the other quantities in the problem. Then write the equation.

Example 1

Keanni throws a stone into a still lake, creating a ring in the water. The diameter of the ring, d, is a linear function of time, t. Five seconds after the stone hits the water, the diameter of the ring is 45 inches. The diameter of the ring increases at a rate of 9 inches per second. Write an equation to represent this situation.

Strategy   **Write an equation in slope-intercept form.**

Step 1   Find the rate of change and the slope.

        The diameter increases by 9 inches per second. This is the rate of change.

        The rate of change gives the slope of the line.

        The slope of the line, m, is 9.

Step 2   Write an equation in slope-intercept form.

        Use slope-intercept form: $d = mt + b$

        Substitute the slope: $d = 9t + b$

        The intercept, b, is unknown.

Step 3   Substitute the given information to find the value of b.

        After 5 seconds, the diameter of the ring is 45 inches. So when $t = 5$ seconds, $d = 45$ inches. Substitute these values into the equation.

        $45 = 9(5) + b$ Multiply.

        $45 = 45 + b$ Subtract 45 from both sides.

        $b = 0$

        Therefore, the equation is $d = 9t$.

Solution   **The diameter of the ring is given by the linear function $d = 9t$, where d is the diameter in inches and t is the time in seconds since the stone hit the water.**

Example 2

Ali's cell phone plan costs $40.00 per month for up to 300 minutes of calls, plus 40 cents for each additional minute. Write an equation that represents Ali's cell phone bill for a month in which he uses more than 300 minutes. Then use the equation to find his bill for a month in which he uses 345 minutes.

Strategy	**Write an equation to represent the situation. Then solve the equation.**
Step 1	Identify the variables.
	Let c = the monthly cell phone bill in dollars. Let m = the number of minutes of calls.
Step 2	Write an equation to represent the relationship.
	Ali's cell phone plan has a flat fee of $40.00 per month plus 40 cents per minute over 300 minutes. If Ali made a total of m minutes of calls, the number of minutes over 300 is $m - 300$. At a cost of 40 cents, or $0.40, per minute, these additional minutes cost $0.4(m - 300)$. Add this amount to the $40.00 flat fee for the total cell phone bill.
	$c = 0.4(m - 300) + 40$
Step 3	Solve the equation for $m = 345$.
	Substitute 345 for m, the number of minutes of calls.
	$c = 0.4(345 - 300) + 40$
	$c = 0.4(45) + 40$
	$c = 18 + 40$
	$c = 58$
Solution	**The equation $c = 0.4(m - 300) + 40$ represents Ali's monthly cell phone bill. If he talks for 345 minutes in a given month, his bill will be $58.**

You can use a system of two linear equations to model two sets of real-world conditions that must be met simultaneously. First define the two variables. Then write two equations to represent the two different relationships between those variables.

Example 3

A movie theater sells tickets for $9.00 each, but students get a $3.00 discount. Yesterday, the movie theater sold 590 tickets and collected a total of $4,680. Write a system of equations that can be used to determine how many tickets were sold to students.

Strategy   **Write a system of linear equations.**

Step 1   Identify the variables.

The variables are the number of student tickets sold and the number of regular tickets sold.

Let s = the number of student tickets sold.

Let r = the number of regular tickets sold.

Step 2   Write one equation.

A total of 590 tickets were sold. So the number of student tickets sold, s, plus the number of regular tickets sold, r, was 590.

$r + s = 590$

Step 3   Write a second equation.

Non-students pay $9.00 for a ticket. Students pay $6.00 ($9.00 minus a $3.00 discount).

For either type of ticket, the amount that the theater collects is equal to the price of the ticket multiplied by the number of tickets sold.

For regular tickets, multiply $9.00 by the number of tickets sold, or $9r$.

For student tickets, multiply $6.00 by the number of tickets sold, or $6s$.

The total amount the theater collected, $4,680, is equal to the amount collected on regular tickets plus the amount collected on student tickets.

$9r + 6s = 4,680$

Solution   **This system of equations that can be used to determine how many tickets were sold to students is $r + s = 590$ and $9r + 6s = 4,680$.**

In a problem-solving situation, be sure to check the reasonableness of your solution.

Example 4

The coach of a high school baseball team bought 6 caps and 8 T-shirts for $140. A few days later, at the same prices, she bought 9 caps and 6 T-shirts for $132.

Write and solve a system of equations to determine the price of a cap and the price of a T-shirt.

Strategy   **Write and solve two equations in the same two variables.**

Step 1   Identify the variables.

The variables are the price of a cap and the price of a T-shirt.

Let c = the price of a cap.

Let t = the price of a T-shirt.

Step 2   Translate from words to symbols.

6 caps and 8 T-shirts for $140: $6c + 8t = 140$

9 caps and 6 T-shirts for $132: $9c + 6t = 132$

A system of equations for determining the two prices is:

$$6c + 8t = 140$$
$$9c + 6t = 132$$

Step 3   Solve this system of equations for t.

First simplify both equations so that the coefficients of c are opposites.

$6c + 8t = 140 \rightarrow$ Divide each term by 2. $\rightarrow \quad 3c + 4t = 70$

$9c + 6t = 132 \rightarrow$ Divide each term by $^-3$. $\rightarrow {}^-3c - 2t = {}^-44$

Add the equations to eliminate c and solve for t.

$$
\begin{aligned}
3c + 4t &= 70 \\
+ \quad {}^-3c - 2t &= {}^-44 \\
\hline
2t &= 26 \\
t &= 13
\end{aligned}
$$

Step 4   Substitute 13 for t into one of the original equations and solve for c.

$$6c + 8(13) = 140$$
$$6c + 104 = 140$$
$$6c = 36$$
$$c = 6$$

Step 5   Check the reasonableness of the solution.

The value of c is 6, or $6 for a cap, and the value of t is 13, or $13 for a T-shirt.

These are realistic prices for buying caps and T-shirts in bulk.

Solution   **The price of a cap is $6, and the price of a T-shirt is $13.**

Coached Example

Manuel has $54 to buy CDs and books. Each CD costs $9, and each book costs $6. He wants to buy exactly 7 items. Write a system of equations that could be solved to determine the number of CDs and the number of books Manuel buys.

Identify the variables.

The variables are _____ and

_____.

Let c represent the number of CDs.

Let b represent the number of books.

Manuel wants to buy 7 items, so $7 =$ _____ $+$ _____.

A CD costs $____. The total amount Manuel pays for CDs is _____ multiplied by _____.

The total cost for CDs is _____.

A book costs $____. The total amount Manuel pays for books is _____ multiplied by _____.

The total cost for books is _____.

Manuel has $54 to spend. Since he wants to spend all his money, this equals the sum of the cost of the CDs and books. That is, $54 =$ _____ $+$ _____.

A system of equations that can be solved to determine the number of CDs and the number of books Manuel buys is _____.

Lesson Practice

Choose the correct answer.

1. Billy works 20 hours per week and earns $8 per hour. Additionally, he receives a commission of 2% of any sales he makes. Which expression represents Billy's total earnings, y, for a week in which his sales were x dollars?

   A. $y = 20 \times 8 + 0.02x$

   B. $y = 20(8 + 0.02x)$

   C. $y = 0.02(20 \times 8 + x)$

   D. $y = 20 + 8 \times 0.02x$

2. Cindy is transporting plants and equipment for her next landscaping job. Her equipment weighs a total of 50 pounds, and each plant weighs 7.5 pounds. The total weight, w, in pounds, of her plants and equipment is related to the number of plants, p, that she brings. What is the total weight of plants and equipment for Cindy's job if she brings 20 plants?

   A. 77.5 pounds

   B. 150 pounds

   C. 200 pounds

   D. 375 pounds

3. Alex has two cats, Buddy and Pepper. The sum of their weights is 16.5 pounds. Buddy weighs 6 pounds less than twice Pepper's weight. How much does Buddy weigh?

   A. 5.25 pounds   C. 8 pounds

   B. 7.5 pounds   D. 9 pounds

4. A teacher placed two orders with an office supply store. The first order was for 200 pencils and 50 markers. The total was $32.50, excluding tax. The second order for 150 pencils and 150 markers totaled $75.00, excluding tax. Which system of equations can be used to determine the price of a pencil?

   A. $p + m = 250$
      $2p + 2m = 107.5$

   B. $p - m = 150$
      $p + m = 300$

   C. $200p + 50m = 32.5$
      $150p + 150m = 75$

   D. $350p + 200m = 107.5$
      $p + m = 300$

5. Joanie went to an amusement park. Admission to the amusement park is $12.00, and ride tickets cost $1.50 each. If Joanie spent a total of $31.50, how many ride tickets did she buy?

   A. 3   C. 18

   B. 13   D. 21

6. Cassidy bought 5 rolls of color film and 4 rolls of black-and-white film for her camera, for a total of $24.00. The black-and-white film costs $1.50 more per roll than the color film. How much does one roll of the black-and-white film cost?

   A. $2.00   C. $3.50

   B. $2.50   D. $4.00

Write and Solve One-Variable Linear Inequalities

SOL: A.5.a, A.5.b, A.5.c

An **inequality** is a mathematical statement showing that one quantity is not equal to another quantity. The following symbols are inequality symbols.

$>$ means "is greater than"	$<$ means "is less than"
$\geq$ means "is greater than or equal to"	$\leq$ means "is less than or equal to"
$\neq$ means "is not equal to"	

The **linear inequality** $x \leq 6$ is read as "x is less than or equal to 6." In set-builder notation, this is expressed as $\{x : x \leq 6\}$. You would read this aloud as "x such that x is less than or equal to 6." You can show all numbers less than or equal to 6 on a number line like the one below.

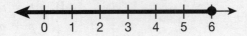

Notice that the graph of this linear inequality has a closed endpoint. This means that 6 is part of the set. An open endpoint on a number means that the number is not part of the set.

A solution to an inequality is the value or set of values that can be substituted to make the inequality true. The properties shown below can be used to solve inequalities.

For all real numbers a, b, and c:

Additive Axiom of Inequality: If $a > b$, then $a + c > b + c$.

Transitive Axiom of Inequality: If $a > b$ and $b > c$, then $a > c$.

Positive Multiplication Axiom of Inequality: If $c > 0$, then $a > b$ if and only if $ac > bc$.

Negative Multiplication Axiom of Inequality: If $c < 0$, then $a > b$ if and only if $ac < bc$.

Solving linear inequalities in one variable is similar to solving linear equations in one variable. When solving linear inequalities, apply the axioms of inequality as follows:

- If you add or subtract a quantity on one side of an inequality, you must add or subtract the same quantity on the other side of the inequality.

- If you multiply or divide by a quantity on one side of an inequality, you must multiply or divide by the same quantity on the other side of the inequality.

- If the number you multiply or divide by is negative, you must switch the direction of the inequality symbol in order to maintain a correct inequality.

Example 1

Solve the inequality and then graph the solution: $-\frac{1}{2}x + 3 < 4$

Strategy   **Isolate the variable. Then graph the solution on a number line.**

Step 1   Subtract 3 from both sides.

$$-\frac{1}{2}x + 3 < 4$$

$$-\frac{1}{2}x + 3 - 3 < 4 - 3$$

$$-\frac{1}{2}x < 1$$

Step 2   Multiply both sides by -2 to make the coefficient of x equal to 1.

When you multiply both sides of an inequality by a negative number, you must reverse the direction of the inequality symbol.

$$-\frac{1}{2}x < 1$$

$$-2\left(-\frac{1}{2}x\right) > -2(1)$$

$$x > -2$$

Step 3   Graph the solution $x > -2$.

The solution does not include -2, so use an open endpoint.

The numbers greater than -2 are to the right of -2 on a number line.

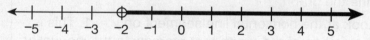

Solution   **The solution set is $\{x : x > -2\}$. The graph is shown in Step 3.**

You may also use a graphing calculator to find the solution to an inequality. Graph each side of the inequality as a linear equation, and identify the section where the inequality relationship is true for both graphs.

Example 2

Solve the inequality and then graph the solution: $3(n - 5) + 8 \leq {}^-4$

Strategy	**Use a graphing calculator to solve. Then graph the solution on a number line.**

Step 1 Define the inequality on a graphing calculator.

Press Y= . Use x for the variable n.

Enter the left side of the inequality, $3(x - 5) + 8$, as Y_1.

Enter the right side of the inequality, $^-4$, as Y_2.

Enter the inequality statement, $3(x - 5) + 8 \leq {}^-4$, into Y_3. (Press 2nd MATH to get the TEST menu, where you can select the appropriate inequality symbol.)

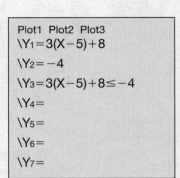

```
Plot1 Plot2 Plot3
\Y₁=3(X−5)+8
\Y₂=−4
\Y₃=3(X−5)+8≤−4
\Y₄=
\Y₅=
\Y₆=
\Y₇=
```

Step 2 Use the graphing calculator to graph and find the solution.

Press GRAPH . Press 2nd TRACE to access the CALC menu and choose number 5: intersect. Move the cursor close to the intersection of the two lines, and hit ENTER three times.

The point of intersection is when $x = 1$.

Step 3 Examine the graph.

Look at the horizontal line segment on $y = 1$. This is the portion of the graph that represents the inequality you entered as Y_3. Where the inequality is true, the y-values on the graph will be at 1, so this line segment shows the solution set for the inequality.

The line extends to the left from 1, so the solution is either $x < 1$ or $x \leq 1$. The calculator does not show an open or closed circle at an inequality endpoint. You must determine the inequality sign by looking at the original inequality. Since the original inequality used $\leq$, the solution set is $x \leq 1$.

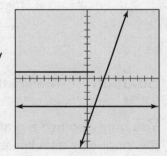

Step 4 Graph the solution set $n \leq 1$ on a number line.

The solution includes 1, so use a closed endpoint.

The numbers less than 1 are to the left of 1.

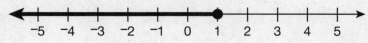

Solution	**The solution is $n \leq 1$. The graph is shown in Step 3.**

Example 3

Tia brings $26 to the grocery store to buy x pounds of trail mix. Each pound of trail mix costs $3. If Tia wants to have more than $8 left over, how much trail mix can she buy? Write and solve an inequality with x. Graph the solution on a number line.

Strategy   **Write an inequality with x. Solve for x and graph the solution set.**

Step 1   Write an inequality with x.

Tia starts with $26.

For every pound of trail mix she buys, she subtracts $3 from her total.

If she buys x pounds of trail mix, she will spend $3x$ dollars. So the amount of money she will have left over if she buys x pounds of trail mix is $26 - 3x$.

Tia wants to have more than $8 left over. The inequality is $26 - 3x > 8$.

Step 2   Isolate the variable to solve the inequality.

$26 - 3x > 8$ Subtract 26 from both sides.

$-3x > -18$ Divide both sides by -3. Reverse the inequality symbol.

$x < 6$

The amount of trial mix purchased must be less than 6 pounds.

Step 3   Graph the solution on a number line.

The graph of $x < 6$ is:

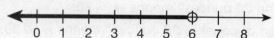

Since the amount of trail mix cannot be less than 0, the solution graph is:

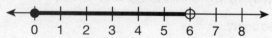

Solution   **Tia must buy fewer than 6 pounds of trail mix.**

If two inequalities are joined by the word *or*, such as "$x \le 2$ or $x > 5$," the solution is all numbers that satisfy either inequality but not necessarily both at the same time. The graph of the solution to $x \le 2$ or $x > 5$ is:

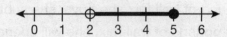

If two inequalities are joined by the word *and*, such as "$x > 2$ and $x \le 5$," the solution is only those numbers that satisfy both inequalities. The graph of the solution to $2 < x \le 5$ is shown below.

Example 4

A shipping company charges a flat fee of $2.95 for packages with weights that are more than 20 ounces and less than or equal to 30 ounces. Express these weight conditions with a compound inequality. Graph the inequality on a number line.

Strategy   **Write a compound inequality. Graph the inequality.**

Step 1   Write a pair of inequalities.

Let w represent the weight of a package.

"More than 20 ounces" means $w > 20$.

"Less than or equal to 30 ounces" means $w \le 30$.

So $w > 20$ and $w \le 30$.

Another way to write this is $20 < w \le 30$.

Step 2   Graph the inequality.

The solution does not include 20. Use an open endpoint.

The solution does include 30. Use a closed endpoint.

A package must satisfy both inequalities, so shade only the area between 20 and 30.

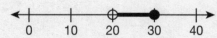

Solution   **Package weights that qualify for the flat fee are represented by the inequality $20 < w \le 30$. The graph is shown in Step 2.**

Coached Example

Jonah is making a cardboard rectangle. The length of the rectangle is 6 inches. The width of the rectangle is $3x$ inches. The area of Jonah's rectangle must be greater than or equal to 54 in.^{2} and less than 108 in.^{2}. The area of a rectangle is found by multiplying its length by its width.

This inequality represents the information given above: $54 \leq 6(3x) < 108$.

What are the possible values of x?

Rewrite the inequality by completing the multiplication. _____

What operation do you need to perform to solve the inequality? _____

What inequality is left after you divide? _____

What whole numbers are included in the solution? _____

Will you need an open or closed endpoint on the left of the graph? _____

Will you need an open or closed endpoint on the right of the graph? _____

Sketch the graph of the solution on the number line below.

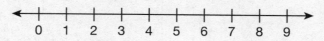

Lesson Practice

Choose the correct answer.

1. What is the solution set for this inequality?

$$\frac{n}{3} + 6 < {}^{-}3$$

   A. $\{n: n < {}^{-}27\}$

   B. $\{n: n < {}^{-}15\}$

   C. $\{n: n < {}^{-}3\}$

   D. $\{n: n < 9\}$

2. What is the solution of this inequality?

$$4 + 2(x - 3) \geq 8$$

   A. $x \geq 3$

   B. $x \geq 3.5$

   C. $x \geq 5$

   D. $x \geq 9$

3. Which graph represents the solution set of this inequality?

$$2(x + 3) < 15 - x$$

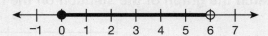

   A. ![number line from -5 to 5, open circle at -3, shaded left]

   B. ![number line from -5 to 5, open circle at -3, shaded right]

   C. ![number line from -5 to 5, open circle at 3, shaded left]

   D. ![number line from -5 to 5, open circle at 4, shaded right]

4. Look at the number line below.

   ![number line from -1 to 7, closed circle at 0, open circle at 6, shaded between]

   Which solution does the number line represent?

   A. $x \leq 0$ or $x > 6$

   B. $x < 0$ and $x \geq 6$

   C. $x > 0$ and $x \leq 6$

   D. $x \geq 0$ and $x < 6$

Use the information below for questions 5 and 6.

Amy has $54 with her when she goes shopping. She wants to buy used CDs that cost $6 each but still have at least $30 left over.

5. Which inequality represents this situation?

    A. $54 - 6c \leq 30$

    B. $54 - 6c \geq 30$

    C. $6c - 54 \leq 30$

    D. $6c - 54 \geq 30$

6. What is the solution set for this inequality?

    A. $\{c: c \leq 4\}$

    B. $\{c: c \geq 4\}$

    C. $\{c: c \leq 14\}$

    D. $\{c: c \geq 14\}$

7. Which graph represents the solution set of this inequality?

$$-3(n + 1) \geq 6$$

    A.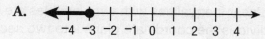

    B.

    C.

    D.

8. A store is having a 50% off sale on all items originally priced between $20 and $80. Sales tax is 6%. Which inequality represents the range of the total cost, in dollars, of one sale item, including tax?

    A. $10.06 \leq x \leq 40.06$

    B. $10.6 \leq x \leq 42.4$

    C. $11.2 \leq x \leq 44.8$

    D. $16 \leq x \leq 46$

Solve and Graph Two-Variable Linear Inequalities

SOL: A.5.a, A.5.b, A.5.c, A.6.a, A.6.b

Linear inequalities with two variables are graphed on a coordinate plane. The linear inequality divides the coordinate plane into two sections, or **half planes**, bounded by the graph of the related linear equation. Only one of those sections contains the solutions.

> **Graphing a Linear Inequality**
> 1. Graph the inequality as if it were a regular line. Use $y = mx + b$ to help you graph.
>   - Use a solid line to show that the line is part of the solution for $\leq$ and $\geq$.
>   - Use a dashed line to show that the line is not part of the solution for $<$ and $>$.
> 2. Choose a test point. If possible, use (0, 0) since it creates numbers that are easy to work with.
>   - If the ordered pair makes the inequality true, shade the half plane that includes that point.
>   - If the ordered pair makes the inequality false, shade the other half plane.

Look at the graph of $y > 3x + 2$ shown below. Since the inequality symbol is $>$, the line is dashed. Substitute the test points (0, 0) and ($^-$2, 3) into the inequality.

(0, 0)	($^-$2, 3)
$y > 3x + 2$	$y > 3x + 2$
$0 \overset{?}{>} 3(0) + 2$	$3 \overset{?}{>} 3(^-2) + 2$
$0 > 2$ FALSE	$3 > ^-4$ TRUE

The points to the left of the line, the part of the coordinate plane containing the point ($^-$2, 3), make the inequality true. So shade that portion of the grid.

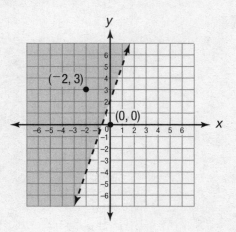

Example 1

Graph the following inequality: $x - 2y \leq 6$

Strategy Graph the boundary line, and use a test point to decide which section of the coordinate plane to shade.

Step 1 Write the inequality in slope-intercept form.

$x - 2y \leq 6$	Subtract x from both sides.
$-2y \leq -x + 6$	Divide by -2, and reverse the inequality symbol.
$y \geq \frac{1}{2}x - 3$	

Step 2 Find two points on the line whose equation is $y = \frac{1}{2}x - 3$.

$b = -3$, so $(0, -3)$ is the y-intercept.

$m = \frac{1}{2} = $ slope

Move up one unit and right two units from $(0, -3)$ to find the second point, $(2, -2)$.

Step 3 Decide if a solid or a dashed line is needed.

The inequality symbol in the original inequality is $\leq$, or "less than or equal to."

The line is part of the solution, so draw a solid line.

Step 4 Substitute the test point $(0, 0)$ into the inequality.

$$x - 2y \leq 6$$
$$0 - 2(0) \stackrel{?}{\leq} 6$$
$$0 \leq 6 \checkmark$$

$(0, 0)$ is part of the solution, so shade the section that contains $(0, 0)$.

Step 5 Graph the inequality.

Solution The graph is shown below.

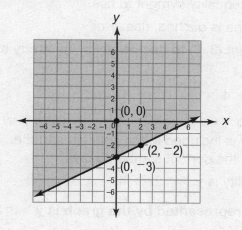

Example 2

Write the inequality represented by the graph below.

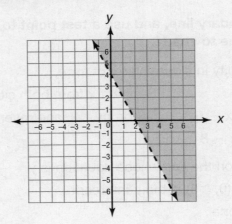

Strategy   **Find the equation of the boundary line. Then use the shading to determine the correct inequality symbol.**

Step 1   Use two points on the line and the slope formula to find the slope of the boundary line.

Two points are (0, 4) and (2, 0).

The formula for finding slope is $m = \frac{y_2 - y_1}{x_2 - x_1}$.

$m = \frac{0 - 4}{2 - 0} = \frac{-4}{2} = {}^-2$

The slope is $^-2$.

Step 2   Use the slope and the y-intercept to write the equation of the boundary line.

The y-intercept is (0, 4), so $b = 4$.

The slope-intercept form of a line is $y = mx + b$.

Since $m = {}^-2$ and $b = 4$, the equation of the boundary line is $y = {}^-2x + 4$.

Step 3   Decide which inequality symbol to use.

Since the line is dashed, use $>$ or $<$.

Use the point (3, 0) to decide which inequality symbol to use. First try $>$.

$y \overset{?}{>} {}^-2x + 4$

$0 \overset{?}{>} {}^-2(3) + 4$

$0 > {}^-2$ ✓

Since (3, 0) is included in the solution and the $>$ symbol makes the inequality true, this is the correct symbol to use.

The inequality is $y > {}^-2x + 4$.

Solution   **The inequality represented by the graph is $y > {}^-2x + 4$.**

You may also use a graphing calculator to graph a two-variable linear inequality.

Example 3

Coach Pace has a budget of $300 to spend on supplies for the school volleyball team. Volleyballs cost $15 each, and uniforms cost $30 each. Write and graph an inequality to represent the solution set for the number of volleyballs, v, and the number of uniforms, u, that Coach Pace can buy.

Strategy   **Write an inequality to represent the situation. Then use a graphing calculator to graph the solution set.**

Step 1   Write an inequality to represent the situation.

Let v = number of volleyballs, and let u = number of uniforms.

Each volleyball costs $15, so the amount spent on v volleyballs is $15v$. Uniforms cost $30 each, so the amount spent on u uniforms is $30u$. The sum of the amounts spent on volleyballs and uniforms must be less than or equal to $300.

$15v + 30u \leq 300$

Step 2   Write the inequality in slope-intercept form.

Let v be the dependent variable (y), and let u be the independent variable (x).

$15y + 30x \leq 300$ Subtract $30x$ from both sides.

$15y \leq {}^-30x + 300$ Divide both sides by 15.

$y \leq {}^-2x + 20$

Step 3   Enter the information into a graphing calculator.

Press ⬛ Y= , and then enter $^-2x + 20$ for Y_1.

Since the inequality symbol is $\leq$, meaning y values are less than or equal to those on the boundary line, you must shade below the boundary line.

Note: If the symbol were $\geq$, it would mean y values were greater than or equal to those on the boundary line, so you would shade above it.

Use the left arrow to move the cursor to the far left side of Y_1. Then hit ENTER until the "shade below" symbol (◣) is displayed. This symbol is a right triangle where the hypotenuse has a negative slope.

Hit ZOOM. In most cases, choosing 6: ZStandard is a good choice since it produces a 10-by-10 window. However, the y-intercept is 20 in this case. You will need to choose 3: Zoom Out or press WINDOW and fill in the appropriate minimum and maximum x- and y-values.

123

View and interpret the graph.

Press GRAPH.

Plot1 Plot2 Plot3
\Y₁=−2X+20
\Y₂=
\Y₃=
\Y₄=
\Y₅=
\Y₆=
\Y₇=

The *x*-intercept is 10, and the *y*-intercept is 20.

Since negative values do not make sense in the context of the problem, only the portion of the shaded section that is in the first quadrant represents the solution set.

Solution   **The inequality $15v + 30u \leq 300$ represents the situation. The graph is the first-quadrant portion of the graph shown in Step 4.**

Note that the calculator will always draw a solid boundary line. You must determine whether the line should be solid or dashed. In Example 3, the inequality symbol was $\leq$, so the boundary line must be solid.

Coached Example

What inequality is represented by the graph below?

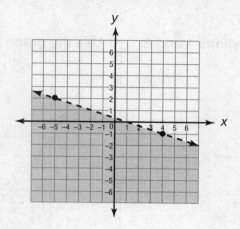

The coordinates of the two points marked on the line are ($^-$5, 2) and _____.

Substitute the values into the formula for finding slope.

$m = \dfrac{y_2 - y_1}{x_2 - x_1} =$ _____ $=$ _____ $=$ _____

The slope of the line is _____.

Use this slope and the coordinates of the point ($^-$5, 2) in the point-slope form of a linear equation.

$y - y_1 = m(x - x_1)$

$y -$ _____ $=$ _____$(x -$ _____$)$

Solve for y to put the equation in slope-intercept form.

$y =$ _____

The dashed line shows that this line _____ included in the solution set.

The point (0, 0) is included in the solution. Use this point to determine which inequality symbol to use. Try $>$. Substitute (0, 0) into the equation you found above.

$y \overset{?}{>}$ _____

$0 \overset{?}{>}$ _____

$0 \overset{?}{>}$ _____

Is the inequality true or false? _____. So the correct inequality symbol to use is _____.

The inequality represented by this graph is _____.

Lesson Practice

Choose the correct answer.

Use the graph below for questions 1 and 2.

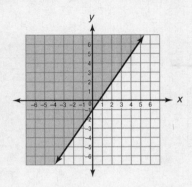

1. Which point is **not** part of the solution set of the inequality represented by this graph?

   A. $(^-3, 2)$

   B. $(0, 0)$

   C. $(1, 1)$

   D. $(4, ^-2)$

2. Which inequality is represented by the graph?

   A. $y > \frac{3}{2}x - 1$

   B. $y \geq \frac{3}{2}x - 1$

   C. $y < \frac{3}{2}x - 1$

   D. $y \leq \frac{3}{2}x - 1$

Use the graph below for questions 3 and 4.

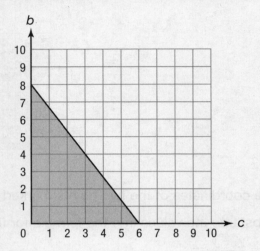

3. Which inequality is represented by this graph?

   A. $b \leq \,^-\frac{3}{4}c + 8$

   B. $b \geq \,^-\frac{3}{4}c + 8$

   C. $b \leq \,^-\frac{4}{3}c + 8$

   D. $b \geq \,^-\frac{4}{3}c + 8$

4. Helen drew this graph to represent the number of $20 computer games, c, and the number of $15 books, b, that she can afford to purchase at the store. According to the graph, which of the following combinations can Helen afford to buy?

   A. 2 computer games and 6 books

   B. 3 computer games and 4 books

   C. 6 computer games and 1 book

   D. 6 computer games and 8 books

5. Melda has \$860 in her account and plans to deposit a minimum of \$50 each month. In other words, after m months, her balance, b, will be at least the sum of her current balance and her monthly deposits. Which inequality represents this situation?

A. $b \geq 860 + 50m$

B. $b \leq 860 + 50m$

C. $b \geq 50 + 860m$

D. $b \leq 50 + 860m$

6. Which of the following points is included in the solution set for $4y > 2x - 12$?

A. $(-2, -5)$

B. $(2, -2)$

C. $(3, -1)$

D. $(6, 0)$

7. Which is the graph of the inequality $2x - 3y \geq -3$?

A.

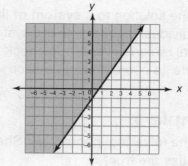

B.

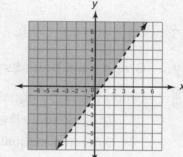

C.

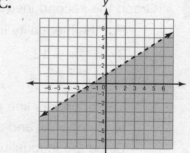

D.

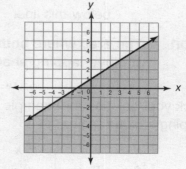

Solve Systems of Inequalities

SOL: A.5.d

To find the solution to a **system of linear inequalities**, find the regions of the plane that satisfy each individual inequality in the system. The solution to the system is the region where the individual regions overlap. To check the solution, choose a point in the common region and substitute its coordinates into each inequality in the system.

Example 1

Graph the following inequalities. Shade the region on the coordinate plane where both inequalities are true.

$$\begin{cases} x \geq {}^-2 \\ x + 3y < 12 \end{cases}$$

Strategy   **Graph each boundary line, shade half planes, and find the overlap.**

Step 1   Graph the first inequality, $x \geq {}^-2$.

The boundary line $x = {}^-2$ is a vertical line at $^-2$ on the x-axis.

Since the inequality symbol is $\geq$, use a solid line and shade the half plane to the right, where the x-values are greater than $^-2$.

Step 2   Graph the second inequality, $x + 3y < 12$.

Put the inequality in slope-intercept form.

$$3y < {}^-x + 12$$
$$y < {}^-\frac{1}{3}x + 4$$

The boundary line $y = {}^-\frac{1}{3}x + 4$ has a slope of $^-\frac{1}{3}x$ and a y-intercept of 4. Since the inequality symbol is $<$, use a dashed line and shade the half plane below this line.

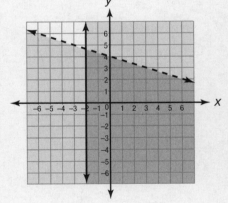

Solution   **The area where both inequalities are true is the overlapping shaded region shown above in Step 2.**

To check your solution for Example 1, you could test the point (0, 0), which lies in the overlapping shaded region.

$x \geq {}^-2$	$x + 3y < 12$
$0 \geq {}^-2$ ✓	$0 + 3(0) \overset{?}{<} 12$
	$0 < 12$ ✓

If the individual solution regions do not overlap, the system has no solution.

Example 2

Graph the following inequalities. Shade the region on the coordinate plane where both inequalities are true.

$$\begin{cases} y > 2x + 1 \\ 2x - y > 4 \end{cases}$$

Strategy   **Graph each boundary line, shade half planes, and find the overlap.**

Step 1   Graph the first inequality, $y > 2x + 1$.

The boundary line $y = 2x + 1$ has a slope of 2 and a y-intercept of 1.

Since the inequality symbol is $>$, use a dashed line and shade the half plane above this boundary line.

Step 2   Graph the second inequality, $2x - y > 4$.

Put the inequality in slope-intercept form.

$$^-y > ^-2x + 4$$

Remember, change the direction of the inequality symbol when multiplying or dividing both sides by a negative number.

$$y < 2x - 4$$

The boundary line $y = 2x - 4$ has a slope of 2 and a y-intercept of $^-4$.

Since the inequality symbol is $<$, use a dashed line and shade the half plane below this boundary line.

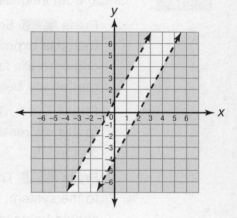

Step 3   Shade the overlapping region.

The individual shaded regions do not overlap, so there is no section where both inequalities are true.

Solution   **There is no solution to this system.**

Note: In Example 2, the boundary lines are parallel and the shading extends in opposite directions. If the lines were not exactly parallel, at some point they would intersect and the shaded regions would overlap.

You may also use a graphing calculator to graph a system of linear inequalities.

Example 3

Graph the solution set for the following system of inequalities.

$$\begin{cases} x + 3y < 6 \\ y \le -\frac{1}{3}x - 3 \end{cases}$$

Strategy   **Use a graphing calculator to graph the system.**

Step 1   Put the inequality $x + 3y < 6$ in slope-intercept form.

$$x + 3y < 6$$
$$3y < {}^-x + 6$$
$$y < -\frac{1}{3}x + 2$$

Step 2   Graph both inequalities on a graphing calculator.

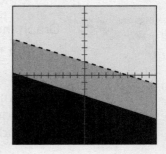

Press [Y=]. Enter $-\frac{1}{3}x + 2$ for Y$_1$. Since y is less than this expression, use the arrow to move the cursor to the far left side of Y$_1$ and press [ENTER] until the "shade below" symbol (▲) is displayed .

Enter $-\frac{1}{3}x - 3$ for Y$_2$. Since y is less than or equal to this expression, select the "shade below" symbol on the left.

Press [GRAPH]. The region of darker overlapped shading represents the solution to the system. The boundary line of the lower inequality, $y \le -\frac{1}{3}x - 3$, should be solid because the inequality symbol is $\le$ and these values are included in the solution set.

Step 3   Test a point from the solution set.

The point $(0, {}^-4)$ lies within the darker shaded region. Substitute these coordinates into both of the original inequalities. Remember, a solution to a system must make both inequalities in the system true.

$$x + 3y < 6 \qquad\qquad y \le -\frac{1}{3}x - 3$$
$$0 + 3(^-4) \overset{?}{\le} 6 \qquad\qquad {}^-4 \overset{?}{\le} -\frac{1}{3}x - 3$$
$${}^-12 < 6 \checkmark \qquad\qquad {}^-4 \le {}^-3 \checkmark$$

Both resulting inequalities are true, so $(0, {}^-4)$ is one solution to the system.

Solution   **The solution to this system of inequalities is the darker shaded region shown in the graph in Step 2.**

Coached Example

Graph the solution set for the following system of inequalities.

$$\begin{cases} x + y > 7 \\ 3y \geq 2x - 6 \end{cases}$$

Put the inequality $x + y > 7$ in slope-intercept form: _____

The boundary line has a slope of _____ and a y-intercept of _____.

Plot the y-intercept and use the slope to find a second point.

The inequality symbol is $>$, so use a _____ line to draw this boundary line.

Shade the half plane _____ the line.

Put the inequality $3y \geq 2x - 6$ in slope-intercept form: _____

The boundary line has a slope of _____ and a y-intercept of _____.

Plot the y-intercept and use the slope to find a second point.

The inequality symbol is $\geq$, so use a _____ line to draw this boundary line.

Shade the half plane _____ the line.

Shade the overlapping region darker.

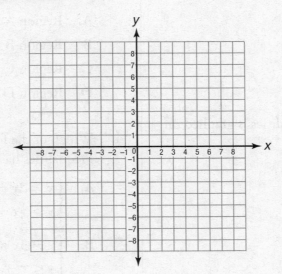

The region with the darker shading is the solution.

Lesson Practice

Choose the correct answer.

The solution to a system of inequalities is shown on the graph below. Use this graph for questions 1 and 2.

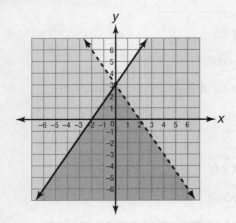

1. Which ordered pair is **not** included in the solution set for the system?

A. $(-2, 0)$

B. $(0, 0)$

C. $(1, -2)$

D. $(2, 0)$

2. Which system of inequalities is graphed on the coordinate grid?

A. $\begin{cases} y < \frac{3}{2}x + 3 \\ y \leq -\frac{3}{2}x + 3 \end{cases}$

B. $\begin{cases} y \geq \frac{3}{2}x + 3 \\ y > -\frac{3}{2}x + 3 \end{cases}$

C. $\begin{cases} y \leq \frac{3}{2}x + 3 \\ y < -\frac{3}{2}x + 3 \end{cases}$

D. $\begin{cases} y \leq \frac{3}{2}x + 3 \\ y > -\frac{3}{2}x + 3 \end{cases}$

3. Which region in the graph below represents the solution to the following system of linear inequalities?

$$\begin{cases} 2x - y > 6 \\ 3y \leq x - 6 \end{cases}$$

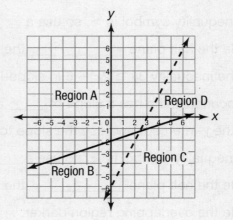

A. Region A

B. Region B

C. Region C

D. Region D

4. Which of the following systems of inequalities has **no** solution?

A. $\begin{cases} x \geq 2y + 6 \\ y > \frac{1}{2}x + 2 \end{cases}$

B. $\begin{cases} y + 3x < 4 \\ y < -3x + 1 \end{cases}$

C. $\begin{cases} 2x + 3y > 6 \\ 3x + 2y \leq 10 \end{cases}$

D. $\begin{cases} x - y \geq 0 \\ y < -4x + 8 \end{cases}$

5. Which graph best represents the solution to the following system of inequalities?

$$\begin{cases} y \leq {}^{-}x + 4 \\ y > {}^{-}1 \end{cases}$$

Use the graph below for questions 6 and 7.

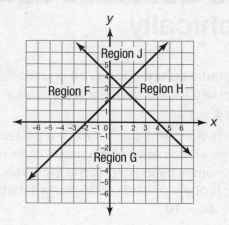

A.

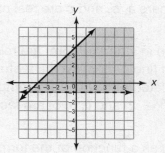

B.

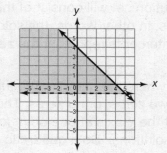

C.

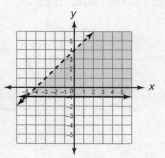

D.

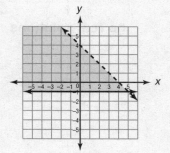

6. Which region represents the solution to the following system of inequalities?

$$\begin{cases} y \leq x + 2 \\ y \leq {}^{-}x + 4 \end{cases}$$

   A. Region F

   B. Region G

   C. Region H

   D. Region J

7. Which region represents the solution to the following system of inequalities?

$$\begin{cases} 3x + 3y \geq 12 \\ 5x - 5y \geq {}^{-}10 \end{cases}$$

   A. Region F

   B. Region G

   C. Region H

   D. Region J

Solve Quadratic Equations Graphically

SOL: A.2.c, A.4.c, A.7.f

A **quadratic equation** is an equation in which the greatest power of any variable is 2. The standard form of a quadratic equation is $ax^2 + bx + c = 0$, where a, b, and c are real numbers and $a \neq 0$.

The factors of the $ax^2 + bx + c$ portion of a quadratic equation in standard form are related to the x-intercepts of the graph of its related function. You can find or confirm the factors of a polynomial by looking at the x-intercepts of the graph of its related function. For example, the graph of $y = x^2 + 3x - 10$ has x-intercepts of 2 and $^-5$, and $(x - 2)$ and $(x + 5)$ are factors of $x^2 + 3x - 10$.

One way to solve a quadratic equation is to write the equation as a function of the form $ax^2 + bx + c = y$ and graph this related function. The real solution set will consist of the x-coordinates of the points where the graph crosses the x-axis. In other words, the solutions will be the x-coordinates of the points where $y = 0$. These x-intercepts represent the **zeros of a function.**

A zero of a quadratic function is the x-coordinate of the point where the graph of the function crosses the x-axis. A quadratic function may have one zero, two zeros, or no zeros. The graph of a quadratic function is a parabola. A parabola can intersect the x-axis at one point (one real solution), two points (two real solutions), or not at all (no real solutions). So a quadratic equation in one variable can have one real solution, two real solutions, or no real solutions.

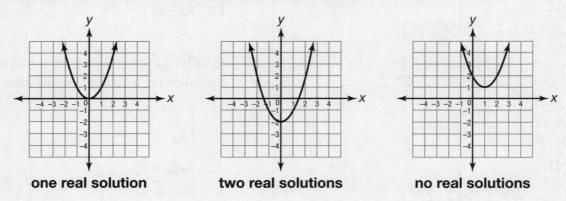

one real solution   two real solutions   no real solutions

Example 1

Make a table and graph to solve $x^2 - 1 = 0$.

Strategy   **Make a table of values and graph the equation. Identify the x-intercepts.**

Step 1   Make a table of values for the related function, $y = x^2 - 1$.

x	$y = x^2 - 1$	y
-2	$y = (-2)^2 - 1 = 3$	3
-1	$y = (-1)^2 - 1 = 0$	0
0	$y = (0)^2 - 1 = -1$	-1
1	$y = (1)^2 - 1 = 0$	0
2	$y = (2)^2 - 1 = 3$	3

Step 2   Graph the points on a coordinate grid, and identify the x-intercepts.

Graph the points $(-2, 3)$, $(-1, 0)$, $(0, -1)$, $(1, 0)$, and $(2, 3)$, and connect them with a parabola.

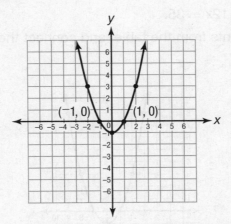

The x-intercepts are $(-1, 0)$ and $(1, 0)$. The x-values of those intercepts are -1 and 1, which are the solutions to the equation.

Solution   The solutions are $x = -1$ and $x = 1$.

The solutions to the quadratic equation in Example 1 can also be expressed using set-builder notation as $\{x : x = -1 \text{ or } 1\}$ or using regular set notation as $\{-1, 1\}$.

Example 2

Find the solutions to $x^2 - 12x + 35 = 0$ graphically.

Strategy   **Graph the related function, and determine the zeros.**

Step 1   Make a table of values for the related function, $y = x^2 - 12x + 35$.

x	$y = x^2 - 12x + 35$	y	(x, y)
3	$y = 3^2 - 12(3) + 35 = 8$	8	(3, 8)
4	$y = 4^2 - 12(4) + 35 = 3$	3	(4, 3)
5	$y = 5^2 - 12(5) + 35 = 0$	0	(5, 0)
6	$y = 6^2 - 12(6) + 35 = {}^-1$	$^-1$	(6, $^-1$)
7	$y = 7^2 - 12(7) + 35 = 0$	0	(7, 0)
8	$y = 8^2 - 12(8) + 35 = 3$	3	(8, 3)
9	$y = 9^2 - 12(9) + 35 = 8$	8	(9, 8)

Step 2   Graph $y = x^2 - 12x + 35$.

Plot the points from the table, and connect them with a curve.

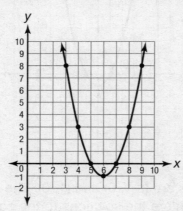

Step 3   Find the zeros of the function.

Find the x-coordinates of the points where the graph crosses the x-axis.

The zeros are $x = 5$ and $x = 7$.

Solution   **The solution set for $x^2 - 12x + 35 = 0$ is {5, 7}.**

Note: In Example 2, you could have also found the zeros by looking at the table and finding the x-values when the y-values are 0.

You can also solve a quadratic equation by graphing the related quadratic function on a graphing calculator and using the calc feature of the calculator to find the x-coordinates of the points where the graph intersects the x-axis.

Example 3

Solve for x: $-3x^2 + 5x = -12$

Strategy   **Rewrite the equation in standard form. Then use a graphing calculator.**

Step 1   Rewrite the equation in standard form.

$$-3x^2 + 5x = -12 \qquad \text{Add 12 to both sides.}$$
$$-3x^2 + 5x + 12 = 0$$

Step 2   Graph the function on your calculator.

Enter $-3x^2 + 5x + 12$ for Y_1.
Then press GRAPH.

Adjust the window, if you need to.

Step 3   Find the zeros of the function.

Press 2nd TRACE to access the CALC menu. Select 2: zero.

The screen asks "Left bound?" Use the arrow keys to move the cursor to the left of one of the x-intercepts. Press ENTER.

The screen asks "Right bound?" Use the arrow keys to move the cursor to the right of that x-intercept. Press ENTER.

The screen asks "Guess?" Press ENTER again.

The calculator shows that one of the zeros is $-1.\overline{3}$, which is the same as $-\frac{4}{3}$.

Repeat this process to find the other zero for the function.

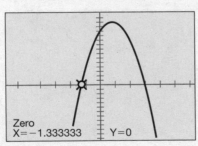

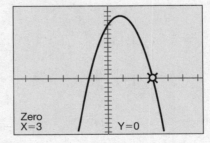

Solution   **The solutions are $x = -\frac{4}{3}$ and $x = 3$.**

Coached Example

Make a table and graph to solve $^-x^2 - 6x - 8 = 0$.

Fill in the missing values in the table.

x	$y = {}^-x^2 - 6x - 8$	y
$^-5$	$y = {}^-(^-5)^2 - 6(^-5) - 8 = {}^-25 + 30 - 8 = {}^-3$	$^-3$
$^-4$	$y =$	
$^-3$	$y =$	
$^-2$	$y =$	
$^-1$	$y =$	

Plot points for the pairs of values in the table. Then connect them to form a graph.

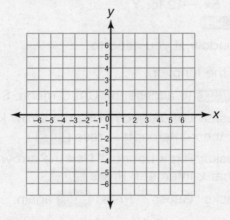

The x-intercepts are (____, ____) and (____, ____).

The solutions to the equation are $x =$ ____ and $x =$ ____.

Lesson Practice

Choose the correct answer.

1. The function $y = x^2 + 8x + 15$ is graphed below.

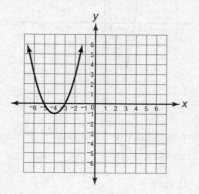

Which are the solutions for the equation $x^2 + 8x + 15 = 0$?

A. $x = {}^-5$ and $x = 0$

B. $x = {}^-5$ and $x = {}^-3$

C. $x = 3$ and $x = 5$

D. $x = 0$ and $x = 15$

2. The function $y = {}^-x^2 + 4$ is graphed below.

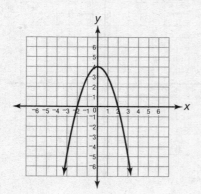

Which is the solution set for the equation $-x^2 + 4 = 0$?

A. $\{{}^-2, 0\}$ **C.** $\{1, 3\}$

B. $\{{}^-2, 2\}$ **D.** $\{2, 4\}$

3. Which graph represents a quadratic equation with exactly one real zero (solution)?

A.

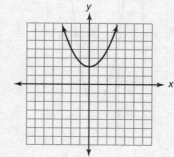

B.

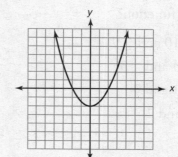

C.

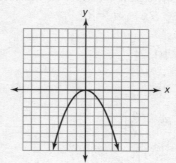

D.

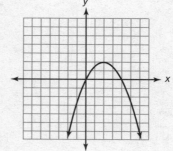

Use the graph of $y = 2x^2 - 7x - 4$ below for questions 4 and 5.

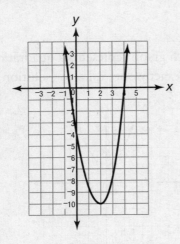

4. Between which two numbers is there a zero for this function?

  A. $^-10$ and $^-9$

  B. $^-4$ and $^-3$

  C. $^-1$ and 0

  D. 1 and 2

5. What is the best estimate of the solution set for $2x^2 - 7x - 4 = 0$?

  A. $\{^-10, 2\}$

  B. $\{^-4\}$

  C. $\left\{^-4, ^-\frac{1}{2}\right\}$

  D. $\left\{^-\frac{1}{2}, 4\right\}$

6. The function $y = 4x^2 + 12x + 5$ is graphed below.

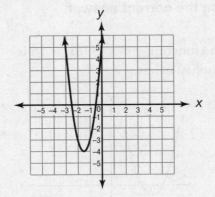

Between which two numbers is there a zero for this function?

  A. 0 and 1

  B. $^-2$ and $^-1$

  C. $^-3$ and $^-2$

  D. $^-4$ and $^-3$

7. Use the coordinate grid below or your graphing calculator. What are the solutions to the equation $x^2 - 6x + 5 = 0$?

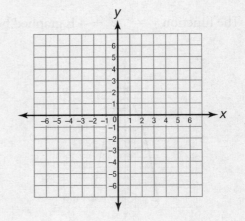

  A. $x = 0$ and $x = 5$

  B. $x = 1$ and $x = 5$

  C. $x = 2$ and $x = 4$

  D. $x = 3$ and $x = ^-4$

Solve Quadratic Equations Algebraically

SOL: A.2.c, A.4.c

Quadratic equations often have two solutions, or two different values of x that make the equation true. One way to solve a quadratic equation is to factor the polynomial if it can be factored. Once a quadratic equation in standard form is factored, you can apply the **zero product property** to solve the equation. This property states:

If $ab = 0$, then $a = 0$ and/or $b = 0$.

> **To solve a quadratic equation by factoring:**
>
> - Get all the terms on one side of the equation so that the value on the other side of the equation is zero.
>
> - Factor the expression completely.
>
> - Set each factor that includes a variable equal to 0, and solve for x in each case. Each answer may be a solution of the quadratic equation.
>
> - Check the solutions in the original equation.

Example 1

Solve by factoring: $x^2 = -3x + 18$

Strategy   **Get all the terms on one side of the equation. Then factor and set each factor equal to 0.**

Step 1   Get all the terms on one side of the equation.

$$x^2 = -3x + 18 \qquad \text{Add } 3x \text{ to both sides.}$$
$$x^2 + 3x = 18 \qquad \text{Subtract 18 from both sides.}$$
$$x^2 + 3x - 18 = 0$$

Step 2   Factor.

$$x^2 + 3x - 18 = 0$$

Find two numbers whose product is -18 and whose sum is 3.

The numbers are 6 and -3 because $6 \cdot (-3) = -18$ and $6 + (-3) = 3$.

Place 6 and -3 in the second position of each binomial.

$$(x + 6)(x + (-3)) = 0$$
$$(x + 6)(x - 3) = 0$$

Step 3 Set each factor equal to 0 and solve.

$$x + 6 = 0 \qquad\qquad x - 3 = 0$$
$$x = {}^-6 \qquad\qquad x = 3$$

The solutions appear to be $^-6$ and 3.

Step 4 Check the solutions.

Substitute $^-6$ and 3 in the original equation.

$$x^2 = {}^-3x + 18 \qquad\qquad x^2 = {}^-3x + 18$$
$$(^-6)^2 \stackrel{?}{=} {}^-3(^-6) + 18 \qquad\qquad (3)^2 \stackrel{?}{=} {}^-3(3) + 18$$
$$36 \stackrel{?}{=} 18 + 18 \qquad\qquad 9 \stackrel{?}{=} {}^-9 + 18$$
$$36 = 36 \checkmark \qquad\qquad 9 = 9 \checkmark$$

Solution The solutions of $x^2 = {}^-3x + 18$ are $x = {}^-6$ and $x = 3$.

You may use a graphing calculator to confirm that you have correctly factored a polynomial.

Example 2

Solve by factoring and express the solution in set notation: $x^2 + 5x + 6 = 0$.

Strategy **Factor the left side of the equation, and confirm the factors using a graphing calculator. Set each binomial factor equal to zero, and solve for x.**

Step 1 Factor the polynomial on the left side of the equation, $x^2 + 5x + 6$.

The factor pairs of 6 are $1 \cdot 6$ and $2 \cdot 3$, so try binomials that include those numbers.

$(x + 1)(x + 6) = x^2 + 7x + 6$, so those factors do not work.

$(x + 2)(x + 3) = x^2 + 5x + 6$, so those factors do work.

So $x^2 + 5x + 6 = (x + 2)(x + 3) = 0$.

Step 2 Use a graphing calculator to confirm that the polynomial is correctly factored.

Store any positive one-digit integer value (not 0 or 1) in x. For example, to store a 4, type 4 `STO▶` x, followed by `ENTER`.

Type in $x^2 + 5x + 6 = (x + 2)(x + 3)$. The "=" sign is under `2nd` `MATH` in the TEST menu.

Hit `ENTER`.

If a 0 appears, this is not the correct answer. If a 1 appears, this is the correct answer. Since a 1 appears, the polynomial is correctly factored.

Step 3   Set each factor equal to 0 and solve.

$$(x + 2)(x + 3) = 0$$

$x + 2 = 0$	$x + 3 = 0$
$x = {}^-2$	$x = {}^-3$

Solution   In set notation, the solution set is $\{{}^-3, {}^-2\}$.

The solutions to a quadratic equation are also known as the **roots** of the quadratic expression if the equation is set equal to 0. The roots are the zeros of the related quadratic function.

Example 3

Find the roots of the equation: $x^2 - 4 = 140$

Strategy   **Write the equation in standard form. Then factor the polynomial and use the zero product property to solve for x.**

Step 1   Write the equation in standard form.

$$x^2 - 4 = 140 \quad \text{Subtract 140 from both sides.}$$
$$x^2 - 144 = 0$$

Step 2   Factor $x^2 - 144$.

This is a difference of two squares, so factor using the special rule
$a^2 - b^2 = (a + b)(a - b)$.

$$x^2 - 144 = x^2 - 12^2 = (x + 12)(x - 12)$$

Step 3   Set each binomial factor equal to 0, and solve for x.

$x + 12 = 0$	$x - 12 = 0$
$x = {}^-12$	$x = 12$

Step 4   Use a graphing calculator to check your answer.

Enter in the related equation $x^2 - 144$ as Y_1 and graph. Check to make sure that the parabola crosses the x-axis at $({}^-12, 0)$ and $(12, 0)$.

Solution   **The solutions, or roots, of $x^2 - 4 = 140$ are $x = {}^-12$ and $x = 12$.**

You can also use a table of values to solve a quadratic equation. The solutions of the equation are the x-values when $y = 0$ in the related quadratic function.

Example 4

Solve this equation using a table of values: $x(x + 5) = 4(x + 3)$

Strategy   **Make a table of values. Find values of x that make the quadratic function equal to 0.**

Step 1   Simplify each side of the equation. Then get all the terms on one side.

$$x(x + 5) = 4(x + 3) \qquad \text{Use the distributive property.}$$
$$x^2 + 5x = 4x + 12 \qquad \text{Subtract } 4x \text{ from both sides.}$$
$$x^2 + x = 12 \qquad \text{Subtract 12 from both sides.}$$
$$x^2 + x - 12 = 0$$

Step 2   Use a graphing calculator to create a table of values for the function $y = x^2 + x - 12$.

Enter $x^2 + x - 12$ as Y_1. Press [2nd] [WINDOW] to access the TBLSET feature. This controls what you see in the table. Try a start value (TblStart) of $^-4$ and an increment (ΔTbl) of 1.

Press [2nd] [GRAPH] to access the TABLE feature. This brings up a table of values for the equation. You will need to scroll down to see additional ordered pairs to find both roots of the equation.

X	Y₁
-4	0
-3	-6
-2	-10
-1	-12
0	-12
3	0
4	8

Step 3   Find values of x that make the function equal to 0.

The values of x that make $y = 0$ are $^-4$ and 3.

Solution   **The solutions of the equation $x(x + 5) = 4(x + 3)$ are $x = {}^-4$ and $x = 3$.**

Coached Example

Solve for x: $x^2 - 8x + 7 = 0$

Factor $x^2 - 8x + 7$.

The second term has a coefficient of _____.

The third term is _____.

Look for a pair of factors with a product of _____ and a sum of _____.

Try _____ and _____.

$(x -$ ____$)(x -$ ____$) =$ _____

Set each binomial factor equal to 0, and solve for x.

$x -$ ____ $= 0$ $x -$ ____ $= 0$

$\quad x =$ ____ $\quad x =$ ____

The solutions, or roots, of $x^2 - 8x + 7 = 0$ are $x =$ _____ and $x =$ _____.

Choose the correct answer.

1. Solve: $x^2 + 2x - 8 = 0$

   A. $x = {}^-8$ and $x = 1$

   B. $x = {}^-4$ and $x = 2$

   C. $x = {}^-2$ and $x = 4$

   D. $x = {}^-2$ and $x = 8$

2. Solve: $x^2 + 5x = 24$

   A. $x = {}^-8$ and $x = {}^-3$

   B. $x = {}^-8$ and $x = 3$

   C. $x = 8$ and $x = {}^-3$

   D. $x = 8$ and $x = 3$

3. Solve: $x^2 - 4x = 60$

   A. $x = {}^-15$ and $x = 4$

   B. $x = {}^-10$ and $x = 6$

   C. $x = {}^-6$ and $x = 10$

   D. $x = {}^-4$ and $x = 15$

4. Solve: $3x^2 - 9x + 6 = 0$

   A. $x = {}^-2$ and $x = {}^-3$

   B. $x = {}^-1$ and $x = {}^-2$

   C. $x = 1$ and $x = 2$

   D. $x = 2$ and $x = 3$

5. Which is the solution set for $4x^2 = 100$?

   A. $\{{}^-5, 5\}$

   B. $\{{}^-10, 10\}$

   C. $\{{}^-20, 20\}$

   D. $\{25\}$

6. Which is the solution set for
   $x^2 - 4x + 5 = 4x - 10$?

   A. $\{{}^-5, {}^-3\}$

   B. $\{{}^-4, {}^-1\}$

   C. $\{1, 4\}$

   D. $\{3, 5\}$

7. Which is the solution set for
   $x(x - 3) = x + 12$?

   A. $\{{}^-3, 5\}$

   B. $\{{}^-2, 6\}$

   C. $\{0, 3\}$

   D. $\{4, 8\}$

8. The height, h, of an object thrown into the air from the top of a 112-foot building is modeled by the function $h = {}^-16t^2 + 96t + 112$, where t is the time, in seconds, since the object was thrown. Note that t cannot be negative in the context of this situation. After how many seconds does the object land on the ground (when $h = 0$)?

   A. 1 second   C. 7 seconds

   B. 3 seconds   D. 16 seconds

Chapter 2 Review

1. Kristen solved the equation $-3(2x + 5) = 9$ using the steps shown below.

   $$-3(2x + 5) = 9$$

   $-6x - 15 = 9$ distributive property

   $-6x = 24$ addition property of equality

   $x = -4$ _____

   What property justifies her final step in the solution?

   A. addition property of equality

   B. subtraction property of equality

   C. multiplication property of equality

   D. division property of equality

2. A line is graphed on the coordinate grid below.

   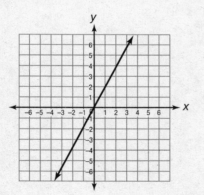

   What is the slope of this line?

   A. -2 C. $\frac{1}{2}$

   B. $-\frac{1}{2}$ D. 2

3. What is the solution to the inequality below?

   $$-2x + 5 \geq x + 8$$

   A. $x \leq -3$

   B. $x \geq -3$

   C. $x \leq -1$

   D. $x \geq -1$

4. The formula for finding the area of a trapezoid is $A = \frac{1}{2}h(b_1 + b_2)$, where h represents the height and b_1 and b_2 represent the lengths of the two bases. Which equation can you use to find the height, h, of the trapezoid?

   A. $h = 2A - b_1 - b_2$

   B. $h = \frac{2A}{b_1 + b_2}$

   C. $h = \frac{A}{2(b_1 + b_2)}$

   D. $h = \frac{A(b_1 + b_2)}{2}$

5. The year 2007 was the 400th anniversary of the founding of Jamestown. Williamsburg was founded 92 years after Jamestown. If j represents the year Jamestown was founded and w represents the year Williamsburg was founded, which system of equations can be used to solve for j and w?

A. $\begin{cases} j = 2007 + 400 \\ w = j + 92 \end{cases}$

B. $\begin{cases} j + 400 = 2007 \\ w = j + 92 \end{cases}$

C. $\begin{cases} j = 2007 + 400 \\ w = j - 92 \end{cases}$

D. $\begin{cases} j + 400 = 2007 \\ w = j - 92 \end{cases}$

6. Use graphing to solve the equation $2x + 4 = x + 1$.

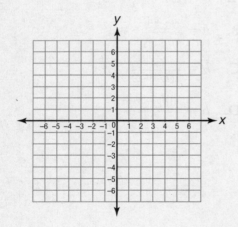

What is the value of x?

A. $x = {}^-4$

B. $x = {}^-3$

C. $x = {}^-2$

D. $x = {}^-1$

7. An inequality is graphed below.

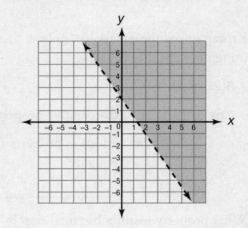

Which inequality is represented by the graph?

A. $y < {}^-\frac{2}{3}x + 2$

B. $y > {}^-\frac{2}{3}x + 2$

C. $y < {}^-\frac{3}{2}x + 2$

D. $y > {}^-\frac{3}{2}x + 2$

8. Which of these graphs could be used to find the solution for the following system of linear equations?

$$\begin{cases} x - y = 2 \\ y = -2x - 4 \end{cases}$$

A.

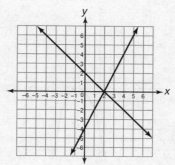

B.

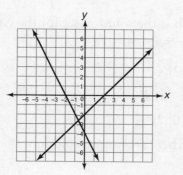

C.

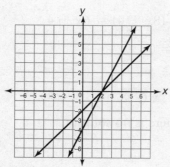

D.

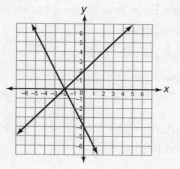

9. If $-3d + 9 < 21$, which axiom of inequality justifies writing $-3d < 12$?

   A. additive axiom

   B. transitive axiom

   C. positive multiplication axiom

   D. negative multiplication axiom

10. Larry is packing for his move. He owns more than 500 pounds of books. He has already packed 110 pounds of those books. If each box can hold 45 pounds of books, which inequality can be used to represent the number of boxes, b, he needs for packing the rest of his books?

    A. $45b - 110 < 500$

    B. $45b - 110 > 500$

    C. $110 + 45b < 500$

    D. $110 + 45b > 500$

11. Which best describes the effect of replacing the slope in the equation $y = \frac{1}{2}x + 8$ with its opposite?

    A. The graph is translated downward.

    B. The graph is reflected across the y-axis.

    C. The graph becomes steeper.

    D. The graph becomes less steep.

12. Which graph best represents the solution to the following system of linear inequalities?

$$\begin{cases} x \le 3 \\ y > \frac{3}{2}x + 3 \end{cases}$$

A.

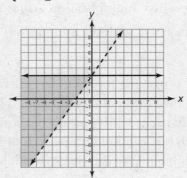

B.

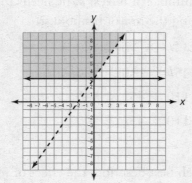

C.

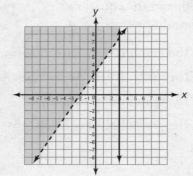

D.

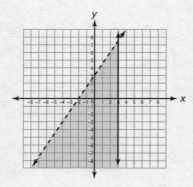

13. Which best describes the graph of a system of linear equations for which there are no solutions?

A. two lines that intersect at exactly one point

B. two lines that intersect at exactly two points

C. two parallel lines

D. two lines that coincide

14. The function $y = {}^-x^2 + 4x - 4$ is graphed below.

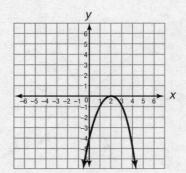

Which is the solution set for the equation ${}^-x^2 + 4x - 4 = 0$?

A. {2}

B. {${}^-4, 2$}

C. {0, 2}

D. There are no real solutions.

15. Solve: $\frac{3}{4}(8x + 4) = 6x + 4$

A. $x = 0$

B. $x = 1$

C. $\{x : x \in \mathbb{R}\}$

D. There is no solution.

16. A line passes through the points $(^-5, 4)$ and $(^-2, 1)$.

    A. What is the equation of this line? Show your work.

    B. Use algebra to solve the system of equations consisting of the equation you found in Part A and the equation $x - 2y = 8$. Show your work.

    C. Graph this system of equations on the coordinate grid below.

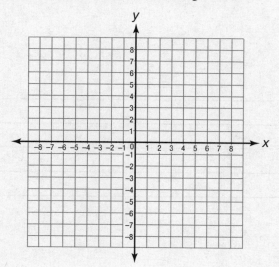

17. A ball is thrown up in the air from the top of a building that is 48 feet tall. The ball's height is modeled by the function $h = -16t^2 + 32t + 48$, where h is the height of the ball, in feet, and t is the time, in seconds, since the ball was thrown.

A. Using a graphing calculator or a table of values, graph this function on the coordinate grid below.

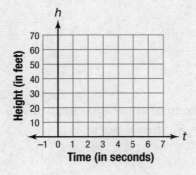

B. How many seconds after being thrown does the ball hit the ground?

_____

C. Completely factor the polynomial $-16t^2 + 32t + 48$. Explain how the graph of the parabola $h = -16t^2 + 32t + 48$ confirms your factorization. What does the portion of the graph between -1 and 0 represent?

_____
_____
_____
_____
_____

Chapter 3

Functions

Determine If a Relation Is a Function

SOL: A.7.a, A.7.f

In the table below, the numbers in the rows represent ordered pairs: ($^-$3, $^-$6), ($^-$2, $^-$4), ($^-$1, $^-$2), (0, 0), (1, 2), (2, 4), and (3, 6). The relationship between the numbers is represented by the equation $y = 2x$. When you double the first number in the ordered pair, the result is the second number in the ordered pair. The graph below shows the coordinates in the table plotted on the coordinate plane and connected with a straight line.

x	y
$^-$3	$^-$6
$^-$2	$^-$4
$^-$1	$^-$2
0	0
1	2
2	4
3	6

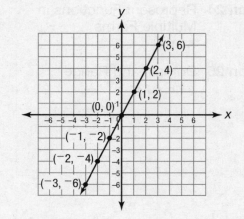

A **relation** is a set of ordered pairs that connects a set of output numbers, or *y*-values, to a set of input numbers, or *x*-values. A **function** is a relation in which each input number, or *x*-value, has one and only one output number, or *y*-value. The table and graph above represent a function. For each *x*-value, there is one and only one *y*-value.

You can use the **vertical line test** to determine if a graph represents a function. If no vertical lines intersect the graph in more than one point, the graph represents a function.

The graph on the left below is a function. The dashed vertical lines each intersect the graph in exactly one point. In other words, each input (*x*-value) corresponds to one and only one output (*y*-value). The graph on the right below is not a function because the dashed vertical lines intersect the graph at more than one point. These pairs of points have the same *x*-value, but have different *y*-values.

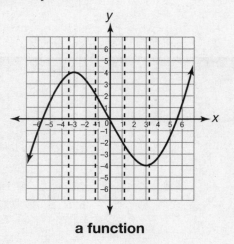

a function

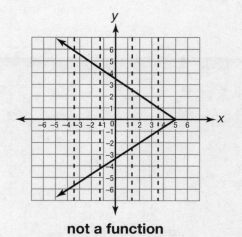

not a function

Example 1

Classify each linear relation as a function or not a function.

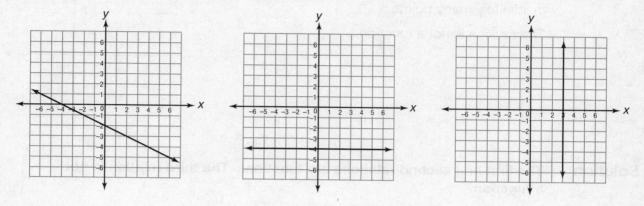

Strategy   **Use the vertical line test. If no vertical lines intersect the graph in more than one point, the relation is a function.**

Step 1	Check the first graph.

No vertical line will intersect the
graph in more than one point.

The relation is a function.

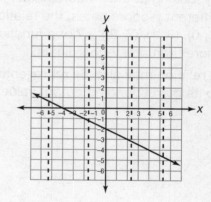

Step 2	Check the second graph.

No vertical line will intersect the
graph in more than one point.

The relation is a function.

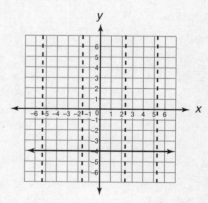

Step 3	Check the third graph.

A vertical line will intersect the graph in infinitely many points.

The relation is not a function.

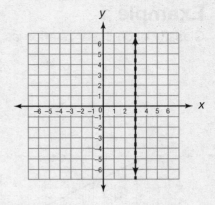

Solution   **The first and second relations are functions. The third relation is not a function.**

If a relation is given as a set of ordered pairs, you can determine whether it is a function by looking at the x-coordinates. If any of the ordered pairs have the same x-coordinate but different y-coordinates, the relation is not a function. For example, the relation $\{(7, {}^-2), (3, {}^-1), (1, 0), (3, 1), (7, 2)\}$ is not a function because the x-coordinates 3 and 7 are each paired with more than one y-coordinate.

A relation may also be represented by an arrow diagram, which shows each input value mapped to its corresponding output value with an arrow.

Example 2

Classify each relation as a function or not a function.

1.

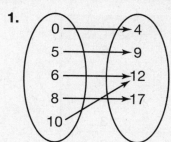

2. {(2, 6), (3, 9), (3, 12), (4, 15), (5, 10)}

Strategy	**Check each set with the definition of function.**
Step 1	List the ordered pairs in the first relation.
	The values are mapped from left to right. So the bubble on the left represents the set of input values, or *x*-values. The bubble on the right represents the set of output values, or *y*-values.
	Follow each arrow to write the ordered pair.
	This arrow diagram shows the set {(0, 4), (5, 9), (6, 12), (8, 17), (10, 12)}.
Step 2	Check whether the first set represents a function.
	The *y*-coordinate 12 is repeated (the arrows from both 6 and 10 map to 12 in the diagram), but none of the *x*-coordinates is repeated.
	So each *x*-coordinate has one and only one *y*-coordinate.
	The relation is a function.
Step 3	Check whether the second set represents a function.
	None of the *y*-coordinates is repeated, but the *x*-coordinate 3 is repeated.
	The *x*-coordinate 3 has *y*-coordinates 9 and 12.
	The relation is not a function.

Solution   **The first relation is a function. The second relation is not a function.**

Not all functions are linear functions. In order for a function to be a linear function, its graph must consist of points that lie on a straight line. You can tell if a table of *x*- and *y*-values represents a linear function by checking to see that the ratio of the change in *y*-values to the change in *x*-values is the same for all ordered pairs. If it is, the points all lie on the same straight line.

Example 3

Classify each relation as a linear function or not a linear function.

x	y
$^-2$	$^-7$
$^-1$	$^-5$
1	$^-1$
2	1
4	5

x	y
$^-3$	6
$^-2$	3
0	0
2	$^-3$
3	$^-6$

Strategy   **Check to see that the ratio of the change in y-values to the change in x-values is the same for all ordered pairs. If it is, the relation is a linear function.**

Step 1 Check the first table.

Find the ratio of the change in y-values to the change in x-values for pairs of ordered pairs.

Since the ratios are equal, the relation is a linear function.

x	y
$^-2$	$^-7$
$^-1$	$^-5$
1	$^-1$
2	1
4	5

$\frac{^-5 - (^-7)}{^-1 - (^-2)} = \frac{2}{1} = 2$

$\frac{^-1 - (^-5)}{1 - (^-1)} = \frac{4}{2} = 2$

$\frac{1 - (^-1)}{2 - 1} = \frac{2}{1} = 2$

$\frac{5 - 1}{4 - 2} = \frac{4}{2} = 2$

Step 2 Check the second table.

Since the ratios are not all equivalent, the relation is not a linear function.

x	y
$^-3$	6
$^-2$	3
0	0
2	$^-3$
3	$^-6$

$\frac{3 - 6}{^-2 - (^-3)} = \frac{^-3}{1} = ^-3$

$\frac{0 - 3}{0 - (^-2)} = \frac{^-3}{2} = ^-\frac{3}{2}$

$\frac{^-3 - 0}{2 - 0} = \frac{^-3}{2} = ^-\frac{3}{2}$

$\frac{^-6 - (^-3)}{3 - 2} = \frac{^-3}{1} = ^-3$

Solution   **The first relation is a linear function, but the second relation is not a linear function.**

Coached Example

Is the relation represented by the equation below a function?

$x = y^2$

Find seven ordered pairs that satisfy the equation.

y	$x = y^2$	x	(x, y)
$^-3$	$x = (^-3)^2 = 9$	9	(9, $^-3$)
$^-2$	$x = (^-2)^2 = 4$	4	(4, $^-2$)
$^-1$	$x = \_\_\_^2 = \_\_\_$	___	(___, $^-1$)
0	$x = \_\_\_^2 = \_\_\_$	___	(___, 0)
1	$x = \_\_\_^2 = \_\_\_$	___	(___, 1)
2	$x = \_\_\_^2 = \_\_\_$	___	(___, 2)
3	$x = \_\_\_^2 = \_\_\_$	___	(___, 3)

Graph the relation on the coordinate grid below. Connect the points. Draw four vertical lines through the graph of $x = y^2$.

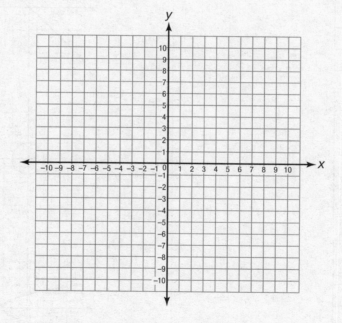

Do any of the vertical lines intersect the graph at more than one point? _____

The equation $x = y^2$ _____ a function.

Lesson Practice

Choose the correct answer.

1. Which table shows a relation that is **not** a function?

A.

x	y
1	9
2	6
3	3
4	0
5	−3

B.

x	y
4	−2
1	−1
0	0
1	1
4	4

C.

x	y
−5	−2
−3	−1
−1	0
4	−1
6	−3

D.

x	y
−1	5
0	2
1	1
2	2
3	5

2. Which graph shows a relation that is a function?

A.

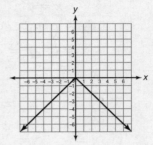

B.

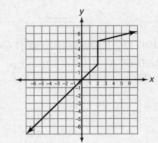

C.

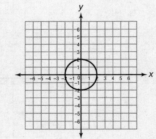

D.

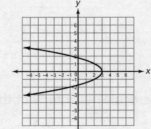

3. Which table shows a relation that is a linear function?

A.

x	y
−2	−9
−1	−3
0	0
1	3
2	9

B.

x	y
0	0
1	1
2	4
3	9
4	16

C.

x	y
−3	8
−1	6
0	4
1	2
3	0

D.

x	y
−4	12
−1	0
0	−4
2	−12
3	−16

4. Which relation is a function?

A. $\{(-3, 2), (-1, 2), (2, -3), (4, 5)\}$

B. $\{(4, 10), (6, 8), (6, 4), (8, 2)\}$

C. $\{(7, 5), (3, 0), (7, -2), (1, -7)\}$

D. $\{(3, -4), (-2, -1), (-1, 2), (3, 8)\}$

5. Which relation is **not** a function?

A. $\{(2, 3), (4, 5), (6, 7), (8, 9)\}$

B. $\{(1, -5), (2, -5), (3, -5), (4, -5)\}$

C. $\{(-4, -3), (-3, -2), (-2, -1), (-1, 0)\}$

D. $\{(6, 4), (7, 5), (8, 6), (8, 7)\}$

6. Which equation is a function?

A. $|y| = x$

B. $y^2 = x - 3$

C. $y^3 = x$

D. $x = -8$

7. A function of x consists of five ordered pairs of the form (x, y). Four of the ordered pairs are shown below.

$$(2, 6), (4, 11), (6, 16), (8, 21)$$

Which could be the fifth ordered pair of the function?

A. $(6, 2)$

B. $(2, 36)$

C. $(10, 8)$

D. $(4, 21)$

Represent Functions in Multiple Forms

SOL: A.7.f

An expression such as $f(x)$ or $g(x)$ is often used to name a function and represents the set of output values for the set of input values represented by x. This is called **function notation**. In the expression $f(x)$, f is not a variable; f is the name of the function. You read the expression $f(x)$ as "f is a function of x" or simply "f of x." In a function equation where the value of y depends on the value of x, $f(x)$ can replace y.

Note: When you use a graphing calculator to graph a function such as $g(x) = 5x + 2$, remember that the expression $g(x)$ can be replaced with y. So when you graph $g(x) = 5x + 2$, use the ▭Y=▭ key and enter $5x + 2$ as Y_1.

Example 1

A function has the equation $y = 3x - 5$. Express this equation in function notation.

Strategy   **Replace the variable y with $f(x)$.**

In the equation, y is expressed in terms of x. So the value of y depends on the value of x.

Replace y with $f(x)$.

Solution   **In function notation, the equation is $f(x) = 3x - 5$.**

Example 2

Write an equation to represent the function described below.

The function value, $f(x)$, is 3 less than 4 times the square of x.

Strategy   **Use key words to translate to equation form.**

Step 1   Identify and interpret key words.

The word "is" represents an equal sign.

The words "less than" indicate subtraction.

The words "4 times" indicate multiplying by 4.

The words "square of x" indicate that x is squared, or raised to the second power.

Step 2   Translate the words into an equation.

Solution   **The function equation is $f(x) = 4x^2 - 3$.**

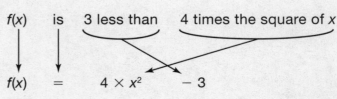

Functions may be represented verbally, graphically, in a table, as an equation, or as a set of ordered pairs. Using what you already know about equations and functions, you can express a given function in all of these different ways.

Example 3

The table below gives three ordered pairs for a linear function.

x	f(x)
−3	4
1	1
5	−2

Graph the function and express it as an equation.

Strategy   **Plot the ordered pairs on a coordinate plane, and draw a line through the points. Calculate the slope, and use point-slope form to write the equation.**

Step 1   Plot the ordered pairs in the table on a coordinate plane, and draw a line through the points.

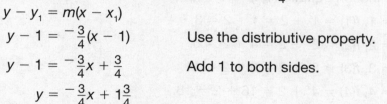

Step 2   Use two points on the line to find the slope.

Use the points (−3, 4) and (5, −2).

$$m = \frac{y_2 - y_1}{x_2 - x_1} = \frac{-2 - 4}{5 - (-3)} = \frac{-6}{8} = -\frac{3}{4}$$

Step 3   Use point-slope form to write the equation of the line, and solve for y to put in slope-intercept form.

Use the point (1, 1) as well as the slope $-\frac{3}{4}$.

$$y - y_1 = m(x - x_1)$$

$$y - 1 = -\frac{3}{4}(x - 1) \qquad \text{Use the distributive property.}$$

$$y - 1 = -\frac{3}{4}x + \frac{3}{4} \qquad \text{Add 1 to both sides.}$$

$$y = -\frac{3}{4}x + 1\frac{3}{4}$$

Step 4   Write using function notation.

$$f(x) = -\frac{3}{4}x + 1\frac{3}{4}$$

Solution   **The graph is shown in Step 1. The function equation is $f(x) = -\frac{3}{4}x + 1\frac{3}{4}$.**

Functions can also be used to represent certain geometric patterns.

Example 4

A pattern of dots is shown below.

What function equation can be used to determine the number of dots in the *n*th figure in the pattern?

Strategy **Identify the pattern, write it algebraically, and verify by counting.**

Step 1 Look for a pattern.

In each figure after the first, there is a square formed by dots, with two additional dots on either side of the base.

The square in the second figure is 2 by 2.

The square in the third figure is 3 by 3.

The square in the fourth figure is 4 by 4.

Step 2 Write an algebraic representation using *n* and *f*(*n*).

The side length of each square is equal to *n*, the number of the figure in the pattern.

The number of dots in each square is equal to n^2.

Two additional dots are next to each square, so the total number of dots in each figure is $n^2 + 2$.

$f(n) = n^2 + 2$

Step 3 Test the function equation $f(n) = n^2 + 2$.

When $n = 1$, $f(1) = 1^2 + 2 = 1 + 2 = 3$.

When $n = 2$, $f(2) = 2^2 + 2 = 4 + 2 = 6$.

When $n = 3$, $f(3) = 3^2 + 2 = 9 + 2 = 11$.

When $n = 4$, $f(4) = 4^2 + 2 = 16 + 2 = 18$.

Count the number of dots in each figure. Figure 1 has 3 dots, figure 2 has 6, figure 3 has 11, and figure 4 has 18. So the function is correct.

Solution **The function $f(n) = n^2 + 2$ can be used to find the number of dots in the *n*th figure in the pattern.**

Functions can also be used to describe algebraic patterns, such as arithmetic sequences. An **arithmetic sequence** is a pattern of numbers in which a common difference is added to each term in order to obtain the next term. Arithmetic sequences are represented by linear functions. The common difference between numbers is the slope, or rate of change, of the function.

To find the nth term (a_n) in an arithmetic sequence, you can use this formula:

$a_n = a_1 + (n - 1)d$, where a_1 represents the first term and d represents the common difference.

Coached Example

Write a formula for finding the nth term in the arithmetic sequence shown below. Find the value of the 7th term in the sequence.

$-2, 3, 8, 13, ...$

Find the common difference, d.

$3 - (-2) =$ _____

$8 - 3 =$ _____

$13 - 8 =$ _____

So $d =$ _____.

The first term, a_1, in the sequence is _____.

The formula for finding the nth term in an arithmetic sequence is $a_n =$ _____.

Substitute the values you found for a_1 and d into the formula.

$a_n =$ _____

Use the distributive property and then combine like terms to simplify.

_____

_____

Use this formula to find the 7th term, a_7. Substitute 7 for n and evaluate.

$a_7 =$ _____ $=$ _____ $=$ _____

The formula that describes this sequence is $a_n =$ _____. The 7th term in the sequence is _____.

Lesson Practice

Choose the correct answer.

1. Which equation represents the function described below?

   The function value, $f(x)$, is 8 more than the product of -2 and x.

   A. $f(x) = -2x - 8$

   B. $f(x) = -2x + 8$

   C. $f(x) = -2(x + 8)$

   D. $f(x) = (-2 + 8)x$

2. Which table represents the function $f(x) = \frac{1}{2}x^2 + 1$?

   A.
x	−2	0	2	4
f(x)	3	1	3	9

   B.
x	−4	0	2	6
f(x)	−7	1	3	19

   C.
x	−1	0	2	8
f(x)	$\frac{3}{2}$	1	5	17

   D.
x	−4	−2	2	4
f(x)	9	3	−3	−9

3. Which formula can be used to find the nth term in the sequence below?

   $$8, 6, 4, 2, 0, \dots$$

   A. $a_n = -2n + 8$

   B. $a_n = 2n + 6$

   C. $a_n = n - 2$

   D. $a_n = -2n + 10$

4. Which of the following graphs represents the function $f(x) = x^2 - 2x - 3$?

   A.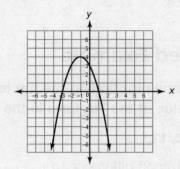

   B.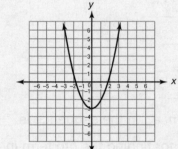

   C.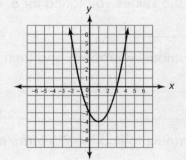

   D.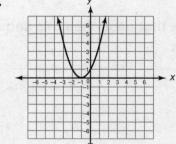

5. A pattern of squares is shown below.

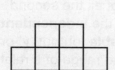 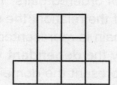 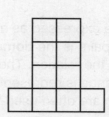 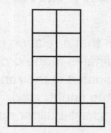

Which function can be used to determine the number of squares in the nth figure in the pattern?

A. $a_n = 2n + 2$

B. $a_n = 2n + 4$

C. $a_n = 4n + 2$

D. $a_n = n^2 + 2$

---

6. Which function is represented by the table below?

x	0	1	2	5
f(x)	−5	−2	1	10

A. $f(x) = x - 5$

B. $f(x) = 2x$

C. $f(x) = 2x - 4$

D. $f(x) = 3x - 5$

7. Which function is represented by the graph below?

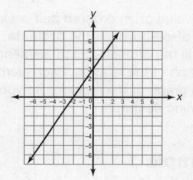

A. $f(x) = {}^-2x + 3$

B. $f(x) = \frac{3}{2}x - 2$

C. $f(x) = \frac{3}{2}x + 3$

D. $f(x) = 3x - 2$

Domain and Range

SOL: A.7.b, A.7.e

Recall that a relation can be expressed as a set of ordered pairs. The set of all the first coordinates in the ordered pairs is the **domain** of the relation; the set of all the second coordinates is the **range** of the relation. The domain is represented by the **independent variable** (input, or x). The range is represented by the **dependent variable** (output, y, or $f(x)$). Set and set-builder notation are often used to represent the domain and range of a relation.

Relation	Domain (Independent Variable, x)	Range (Dependent Variable, y)
(1, 2), (2, 4), (3, 8)	{1, 2, 3}	{2, 4, 8}
(1, 3), (2, 4), (3, 3), (4, 4)	{1, 2, 3, 4}	{3, 4}

When a relation represents a particular situation or has a context, the y-value depends on the value chosen for the independent (x) variable. For example, the amount of money, in dollars, owed on an electric bill depends on the amount of electricity, in kilowatt-hours, used. The number of kilowatt-hours is the independent variable, and the amount of money owed is the dependent variable.

The x-value of an ordered pair is also known as the **abscissa**, and the y-value of an ordered pair is also known as the **ordinate**. For example, in the ordered pair (2, 3), 2 is the abscissa and 3 is the ordinate. Each element in the domain of a relation is the abscissa of a point on the graph of the relation. Each element in the range of a relation is the ordinate of a point on the graph of the relation. So you can determine the domain and range of a relation by examining its graph.

Example 1

The graph below represents a function. What are the domain and range? Express both in set-builder notation.

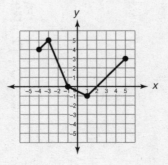

Strategy   **Analyze the graph.**

Step 1	Identify the domain.

The *x*-values, or abscissas, of all points along the function represent the domain.

The point farthest to the left on the graph is (−4, 4). So −4 is the minimum value in the domain.

The point farthest to the right on the graph is (5, 3). So 5 is the maximum value in the domain.

The graph is continuous, so all *x*-values between the minimum and maximum are included.

The domain is −4 ≤ *x* ≤ 5.

In set-builder notation, this is written {*x* : −4 ≤ *x* ≤ 5}.

Step 2	Identify the range.

The *y*-values, or ordinates, of all points along the function represent the range.

The lowest point on the graph is (1, −1). So −1 is the minimum value in the range.

The highest point on the graph is (−3, 5). So 5 is the maximum value in the range.

The graph is continuous, so all *y*-values between the minimum and maximum are included.

The range is −1 ≤ *y* ≤ 5.

In set-builder notation, this is written {*y* : −1 ≤ *y* ≤ 5}.

Solution   **The domain is {*x* : −4 ≤ *x* ≤ 5}. The range is {*y* : −1 ≤ *y* ≤ 5}.**

Unlike the piecewise function shown in Example 1, any linear function has a domain of all real numbers because its graph is a straight line that continues infinitely to the left and right, even if the line is very steep. Any linear function that is not horizontal has a range of all real numbers because its graph is a straight line that continues infinitely upward and downward.

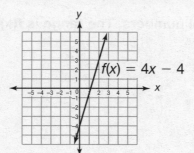

domain: all real numbers
range: all real numbers

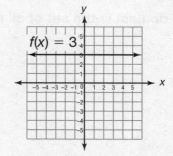

domain: all real numbers
range: *f*(*x*) = 3

Example 2

Below is the graph of $f(x) = \frac{1}{4}x^2 - 5$. Identify the domain and range of the function.

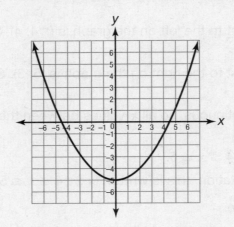

Strategy   **Use the definitions of domain and range.**

Step 1   Identify the domain.

The independent variable is x.

The arrows show that the parabola continues in both directions. So all x-values to the left and to the right of what you see on the graph are included.

The domain is the set of all real numbers.

Step 2   Identify the range.

The dependent variable is $f(x)$.

The lowest $f(x)$-value on the graph is -5. The arrows show that the parabola continues up. So all $f(x)$-values above what you see on the graph are included.

The range is the set of all real numbers greater than or equal to -5, or $f(x) \geq -5$.

Solution   **The domain is the set of all real numbers. The range is $f(x) \geq -5$.**

You can also determine the domain and range of basic linear and quadratic functions by looking at their equations.

Example 3

What are the domain and range of the function $g(x) = x^2 + 3$?

Strategy   **Consider possible x- and $g(x)$-values, using the given equation.**

Step 1   Identify the domain.

The domain is the set of x-values for which the function is defined.

Any real-number value could be substituted for x in this equation and produce a real-number $g(x)$-value. So the function $g(x) = x^2 + 3$ is defined for all real values of x.

The domain is all real numbers, or $\{x : x \in \mathbb{R}\}$.

Step 2   Identify the range.

The range is the set of resulting $g(x)$-values for the set of x-values in the domain.

When a number is squared, its value is always nonnegative. For all negative x-values as well as all positive x-values, x^2 is positive. As the absolute value of x increases infinitely, the value of x^2 increases infinitely. The minimum value of x^2 is 0, when $x = 0$. So the minimum value of $x^2 + 3$ is 3.

The minimum $g(x)$-value is 3, and $g(x)$-values increase infinitely from there.

The range is all real numbers greater than or equal to 3.

Solution   **For the function $g(x) = x^2 + 3$, the domain is $\{x : x \in \mathbb{R}\}$ and the range is $\{g(x) : g(x) \geq 3\}$.**

A domain value is any element in the function's domain. When you are given a function in equation form and a domain value, you can substitute the domain value in the function equation to find the corresponding range value. This is called evaluating a function for a given domain value.

Example 4

If $f(x) = 2x^2 - x - 1$, what is $f(-3)$?

Strategy   Substitute -3 for x in the function equation, and simplify to find $f(-3)$.

Step 1   Substitute -3 for x in the function equation.

$$f(x) = 2x^2 - x - 1$$
$$f(-3) = 2(-3)^2 - (-3) - 1$$

Step 2   Use the order of operations to simplify the right side of the function equation.

$f(-3) = 2(-3)^2 - (-3) - 1$	Evaluate the exponent.
$f(-3) = 2(9) - (-3) - 1$	Multiply.
$f(-3) = 18 + 3 - 1$	Add and subtract from left to right.
$f(-3) = 20$	

Solution   If $f(x) = 2x^2 - x - 1$, then $f(-3) = 20$.

By finding the unique corresponding value in the range for a given value in the domain, as in Example 4 above, you are identifying the abscissa and ordinate of a point in the relation. For each x in the domain of f, x is a member of the input of the function, $f(x)$ is a member of the output of the function, and the ordered pair $(x, f(x))$ is a member of f.

Coached Example

What points with x-values of -2 and 2 are members of the function $f(x) = 5x - 2$?

First you must find $f(\underline{\quad})$ and $f(\underline{\quad})$.

To find $f(-2)$, replace x with $\underline{\quad}$ in the equation $f(x) = 5x - 2$.

$f(-2) = 5(\underline{\quad}) - 2 = \underline{\quad} - 2 = \underline{\quad}$

So one point in the function $f(x) = 5x - 2$ is $(-2, \underline{\quad})$.

To find $f(2)$, replace x with $\underline{\quad}$ in the equation $f(x) = 5x - 2$.

$f(2) = 5(\underline{\quad}) - 2 = \underline{\quad} - 2 = \underline{\quad}$

So another point in the function $f(x) = 5x - 2$ is $(2, \underline{\quad})$.

The points in the function $f(x) = 5x - 2$ that have x-values of -2 and 2 are $(\underline{\quad}, \underline{\quad})$ and $(\underline{\quad}, \underline{\quad})$.

Lesson Practice

Choose the correct answer.

1. A relation is shown below.

    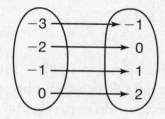

    What is the domain of this relation?

    A. $\{-3, -2\}$

    B. $\{-3, -2, -1, 0\}$

    C. $\{-1, 0, 1, 2\}$

    D. $\{-3, -2, -1, 0, 1, 2\}$

2. If $g(x) = -x^2 + 9$, what is $g(4)$?

    A. -25

    B. 1

    C. -7

    D. -25

3. A linear function is represented by the graph below.

    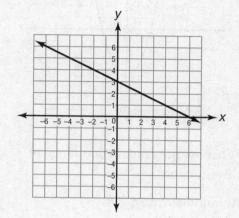

    What are the domain and range of this function?

    A. domain: $\{x : x \le 6\}$;
        range: $\{y : y \le 6\}$

    B. domain: $\{x : x \le 6\}$;
        range: $\{y : y \ge 0\}$

    C. domain: $\{x : x \in \mathbb{R}\}$;
        range: $\{y : y \ge 0\}$

    D. domain: $\{x : x \in \mathbb{R}\}$;
        range: $\{y : y \in \mathbb{R}\}$

4. What is the range of the function $f(x) = x - 8$?

    A. $f(x) \le -8$

    B. $f(x) \ge -8$

    C. $f(x) \ge 8$

    D. $\{f(x) : f(x) \in \mathbb{R}\}$

5. A function is represented by the graph below.

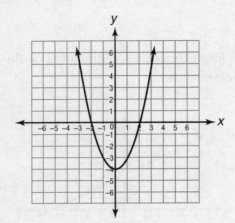

What are the domain and range of this function?

A. domain: $x \geq {}^-4$;
   range: all real numbers

B. domain: all real numbers;
   range: $f(x) \geq {}^-4$

C. domain: $^-2 \leq x \leq 2$;
   range: $f(x) \geq {}^-4$

D. domain: all real numbers;
   range: all real numbers

6. What are the domain and range of the function $g(x) = {}^-x^2$?

A. domain: $\{x : x \geq 0\}$;
   range: $\{g(x) : g(x) \leq 0\}$

B. domain: $\{x : x \in \mathbb{R}\}$;
   range: $\{g(x): g(x) \leq 0\}$

C. domain: $\{x : x \in \mathbb{R}\}$;
   range: $\{g(x): g(x) \geq 0\}$

D. domain: $\{x : x \in \mathbb{R}\}$;
   range: $\{g(x) : g(x) \in \mathbb{R}\}$

7. Which of the following ordered pairs is a member of the function $f(x) = 3x^2 - x$?

A. $(^-2, 14)$

B. $(^-1, 2)$

C. $(2, 12)$

D. $(3, 6)$

8. The function $f(x) = 1,500 - 150x$ gives the amount Oliver owes for his television set after x months of paying installments. What is $f(7)$, the amount Oliver owes after paying 7 monthly installments?

A. $450

B. $550

C. $750

D. $1,050

Zeros and Intercepts of Functions

SOL: A.7.c, A.7.d

As you already learned, a zero of a quadratic function is the x-coordinate of a point where the graph crosses the x-axis. The zero(s) of a function of any type are the x-coordinates of all points where the graph of the function crosses the x-axis.

An x-intercept of a function is a point where the function intersects the x-axis, so the x-value of an x-intercept is also a zero of the function. The y-intercept of a function is the point where the function intersects the y-axis. A function will always have at most one y-intercept but may have zero, one, or more than one x-intercepts, or zeros.

Example 1

Identify the intercepts and zero for the function $f(x) = -\frac{1}{2}x + 2$, which is graphed below.

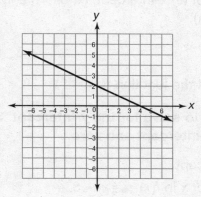

Strategy	Use the definitions of x-intercept, y-intercept, and zero of a function.

Step 1 Label the intercepts on the graph.

The graph crosses the x-axis at (4, 0).

The graph crosses the y-axis at (0, 2).

Step 2 Identify the zeros of the function.

The zero is the x-coordinate of the point where the graph crosses the x-axis.

The graph crosses the x-axis at (4, 0).

The value of $f(x)$ is 0 at the x-intercept, where $x = 4$.

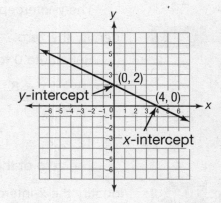

Step 3   Check your solution.

Use the equation $f(x) = -\frac{1}{2}x + 2$ to check that the x-value of 4 makes $f(x) = 0$.

$f(4) \overset{?}{=} -\frac{1}{2}(4) + 2$

$f(4) \overset{?}{=} -2 + 2$

$f(4) = 0 \checkmark$

The zero of the function is 4.

Solution   **The x-intercept is (4, 0), the y-intercept is (0, 2), and the zero of the function is 4.**

An object x in the domain of a function f is a zero of the function if and only if $f(x) = 0$. To solve algebraically for the zero(s) of a function, substitute 0 for $f(x)$ and solve for x. Each zero also represents the x-value of an x-intercept, $(x, 0)$. To solve for the y-intercept, $(0, f(x))$, substitute 0 for x and solve for $f(x)$.

Example 2

Identify the intercepts and zero of the function $f(x) = \frac{2}{3}x - 8$.

Strategy   **Substitute 0 for x to solve for the y-intercept. Substitute 0 for $f(x)$ to solve for the x-intercept and zero.**

Step 1   Identify the y-intercept.

Substitute 0 for x in $f(x) = \frac{2}{3}x - 8$.

$f(0) = \frac{2}{3}(0) - 8$

$f(0) = -8$

The y-intercept is $(0, -8)$.

Step 2   Identify the zero.

Substitute 0 for $f(x)$ in $f(x) = \frac{2}{3}x - 8$.

$0 = \frac{2}{3}x - 8$ Add 8 to both sides.

$8 = \frac{2}{3}x$ Multiply both sides by $\frac{3}{2}$.

$12 = x$

The zero of the function is 12.

Step 3   Identify the x-intercept.

The zero of the function is the x-value of the x-intercept.

The x-intercept is $(12, 0)$.

Solution   **The x-intercept is (12, 0), the y-intercept is (0, −8), and the zero of the function is 12.**

A quadratic function may have no, one, or two zeros.

Example 3

Identify the intercepts and zeros of the function $f(x) = x^2 - 4x - 5$, which is graphed below.

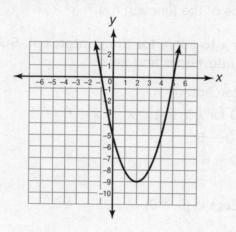

Strategy   Use the definitions of x-intercept, y-intercept, and zeros of a function.

Step 1   Label the intercepts on the graph.

The graph crosses the x-axis at $(-1, 0)$ and $(5, 0)$.

The graph crosses the y-axis at $(0, -5)$.

Step 2   Identify the zeros of the function.

The zeros are the values of x that make $f(x) = 0$.

By looking at the x-intercepts, you can see that the output value is 0 when $x = -1$ and when $x = 5$.

Use the equation $f(x) = x^2 - 4x - 5$ to check that those values make $f(x) = 0$.

$f(-1) \overset{?}{=} (-1)^2 - 4(-1) - 5$ $f(5) \overset{?}{=} 5^2 - 4(5) - 5$

$f(-1) \overset{?}{=} 1 + 4 - 5$ $f(5) \overset{?}{=} 25 - 20 - 5$

$f(-1) = 0 \checkmark$ $f(5) = 0 \checkmark$

The zeros of the function are -1 and 5.

Solution   The x-intercepts are $(-1, 0)$ and $(5, 0)$. The y-intercept is $(0, -5)$. The zeros of the function are -1 and 5.

To solve for the zeros of a quadratic function algebraically, you may need to factor the quadratic and use the zero product property.

Example 4

Identify the intercepts and zeros of the function $f(x) = x^2 + x - 6$.

Strategy   **Substitute 0 for x to solve for the y-intercept. Substitute 0 for $f(x)$ to solve for the x-intercepts and zeros.**

Step 1   Identify the y-intercept.

Substitute 0 for x in $f(x) = x^2 + x - 6$.

$f(0) = 0^2 + 0 - 6$

$f(0) = 0 + 0 - 6$

$f(0) = {}^-6$

The y-intercept is $(0, {}^-6)$.

Step 2   Identify the zeros.

Substitute 0 for $f(x)$ in $f(x) = x^2 + x - 6$. Then factor the quadratic and use the zero product property to solve for x.

$0 = x^2 + x - 6$

Find two values whose product is $^-6$ and whose sum is 1. The numbers 3 and $^-2$ have a product of $^-6$ and a sum of 1. So $x^2 + x - 6$ factors as $(x + 3)(x - 2)$.

$0 = (x + 3)(x - 2)$

Set each factor equal to 0 and solve for x.

$x + 3 = 0$	$x - 2 = 0$
$x = {}^-3$	$x = 2$

The zeros of the function are $^-3$ and 2.

Step 3   Identify the x-intercepts.

The zeros of the function are the x-values of the x-intercepts.

The x-intercepts are $(^-3, 0)$ and $(2, 0)$.

Solution   **The x-intercepts are $(^-3, 0)$ and $(2, 0)$. The y-intercept is $(0, {}^-6)$. The zeros of the function are $^-3$ and 2.**

Coached Example

Below are the graphs of $f(x) = {}^-x^2 + 9$ and $g(x) = x^2 - 9$.

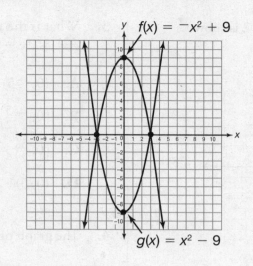

Compare the intercepts of the two quadratic functions.

The y-intercept is the point at which a graph crosses the y-axis.

The graph of $f(x) = {}^-x^2 + 9$ crosses the y-axis at $(0, \underline{\hspace{1cm}})$.

The graph of $g(x) = x^2 - 9$ crosses the y-axis at $(0, \underline{\hspace{1cm}})$.

The x-intercepts are the points at which a graph crosses the x-axis.

The x-intercepts are the same for both graphs: $(\underline{\hspace{1cm}}, 0)$ and $(\underline{\hspace{1cm}}, 0)$.

Even though both graphs have identical ____-intercepts, they have different ____-intercepts.

Choose the correct answer.

1. The graph of $r(x) = 2x - 2$ is shown below.

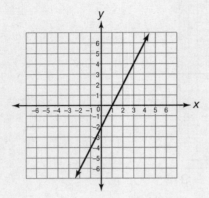

What are the x- and y-intercepts of this function?

A. x-intercept: $(2, 0)$; y-intercept: $(0, {}^-2)$
B. x-intercept: $(1, 0)$; y-intercept: $(0, {}^-2)$
C. x-intercept: $({}^-2, 0)$; y-intercept: $(0, 1)$
D. x-intercept: $({}^-2, 0)$; y-intercept: $(0, 2)$

2. What is the zero of the function $f(x) = {}^-3x + 6$?

A. -3
B. -2
C. 2
D. 6

3. What is the y-intercept of the function $g(x) = 2x - 5$?

A. $(0, {}^-5)$
B. $\left(0, -\dfrac{5}{2}\right)$
C. $\left(0, \dfrac{5}{2}\right)$
D. $(0, 5)$

4. The graph of $f(x) = x^2 - 4$ is shown below.

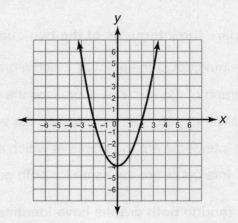

What are the zeros of the function?

A. -2 and -4
B. -2 and 0
C. -2 and 2
D. 0 and -4

Use the graph of the functions
$f(x) = 2x^2 + 6$ and $g(x) = -\frac{2}{3}x^2 + 6$
shown below for questions 5 and 6.

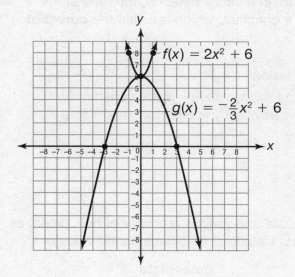

5. How many zeros does the function
   $f(x) = 2x^2 + 6$ have?

   A. 0

   B. 1

   C. 2

   D. 3

6. Which statement is true of the functions
   $f(x)$ and $g(x)$?

   A. They have the same zero, 6.

   B. They have the same x-intercepts,
      -3 and 3.

   C. They have the same y-intercept, 6.

   D. They have the same zeros, -3 and 3.

7. What are the zeros of the function
   $r(x) = x^2 - 9x + 20$?

   A. -5 and -4

   B. -5 and 4

   C. -4 and 5

   D. 4 and 5

8. What is the y-intercept of the function
   $h(x) = x^2 - 6x + 8$?

   A. $(0, -4)$

   B. $(0, 2)$

   C. $(0, 4)$

   D. $(0, 8)$

9. Which of the following is true of the
   function $f(x) = \frac{1}{5}x + 4$?

   A. The y-intercept is $\left(0, \frac{1}{5}\right)$.

   B. The y-intercept is $(4, 0)$.

   C. There is no x-intercept.

   D. There is one x-intercept, at $(-20, 0)$.

Direct Variation

SOL: A.8

A **direct variation** is an example of a linear function. In a direct variation, the ratio of the dependent variable to the independent variable is a constant, which is called the **constant of proportionality** or the **constant of variation**.

> ### Direct Variation
> A direct variation is a function in the form $y = kx$, where k is the constant of proportionality and $k \neq 0$. In this case, we say that y is directly proportional to x or that y varies directly with x.

Example 1

Ani compared the prices of various packages of pasta and various amounts of bulk pasta, as shown in the tables. Does either table show a direct variation? If so, what is the value of k?

Packaged Pasta	
Weight in Pounds (x)	Price in Dollars (y)
3.2	8.96
4.6	13.34
5.8	14.50
7.2	22.32

Bulk Pasta	
Weight in Pounds (x)	Price in Dollars (y)
4.2	10.50
5.8	14.50
6.6	16.50
10.2	25.50

Strategy Find the ratio of y to x for each pair of values in the tables.

Step 1 Determine if the values for packaged pasta vary directly.

In a direct variation, $y = kx$, so $k = \frac{y}{x}$. Find the ratio $\frac{y}{x}$ for each pair.

$\frac{8.96}{3.2} = 2.8$ $\frac{13.34}{4.6} = 2.9 \leftarrow$ different ratio

The ratio is not constant, so this table does not show a direct variation.

Step 2 Determine if the values for bulk pasta vary directly.

$\frac{10.5}{4.2} = 2.5$ $\frac{14.5}{5.8} = 2.5$ $\frac{16.5}{6.6} = 2.5$ $\frac{25.5}{10.2} = 2.5$

The ratio is constant, so $k = 2.5$ and the table shows a direct variation.

Solution **The bulk pasta table shows a direct variation with $k = 2.5$.**

Example 2

An algebra teacher draws two graphs on the board. Which graph shows a direct variation? What is the constant of proportionality?

Graph 1

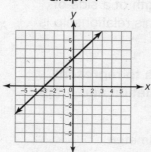

Graph 2

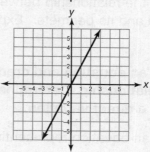

Strategy   **Find the ratio of *y* to *x* for at least two points on each line.**

Step 1   Find the ratio $\frac{y}{x}$ for two points on the line in graph 1.

Try $(-3, 0)$ and $(1, 4)$.

For $(-3, 0)$, the ratio is $\frac{0}{-3} = 0$.

For $(1, 4)$, the ratio is $\frac{4}{1} = 4 \leftarrow$ different ratio.

The ratio $\frac{y}{x}$ is not constant. So graph 1 does not show a direct variation.

Step 2   Find the ratio $\frac{y}{x}$ for two points on the line in graph 2.

Try $(-2, -4)$ and $(1, 2)$.

For $(-2, -4)$, the ratio is $\frac{-4}{-2} = 2$.

For $(1, 2)$, the ratio is $\frac{2}{1} = 2 \leftarrow$ same ratio.

The ratio $\frac{y}{x}$ is constant for both points.

Since all points on a straight line change by the same constant rate, the slope, you only need to test two points.

Graph 2 shows a direct variation with $k = 2$.

Solution   **Graph 2 shows a direct variation. The constant of proportionality, *k*, is 2.**

Note: If the graph of a function is a nonvertical straight line that passes through the origin, the function is a direct variation. The slope of the line is the constant of proportionality, *k*, and the *y*-intercept is (0, 0).

Example 3

A regular pentagon, like the one shown on the right, has five sides that are all the same length. Write an equation representing the perimeter of the pentagon, using the variables x and y. Then create a graph to represent the relationship between the length of a side of the regular pentagon and its perimeter. Explain why this relationship is a direct variation.

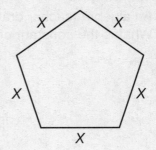

Strategy **Write an equation and create a graph to represent the relationship. Determine if the equation and graph show a direct variation.**

Step 1 Write an equation representing the perimeter.

Each side of the pentagon is x units long.

You can add the lengths of all five sides to find the perimeter, y.

$$y = x + x + x + x + x = 5x$$

The equation $y = 5x$ represents this situation.

Step 2 Create a graph.

The equation $y = 5x$ is in slope-intercept form.

The slope is 5, and the y-intercept is $(0, 0)$.

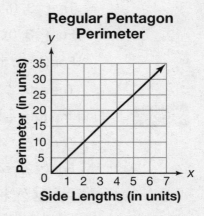

Step 3 Explain why the relationship is a direct variation.

The equation $y = 5x$ is in the form $y = kx$.

The constant of proportionality is 5.

Also, the graph is a nonvertical straight line that passes through the origin. So it shows a direct variation.

Solution **The equation $y = 5x$ and the graph in Step 2 represent the relationship between the length of one side of a regular pentagon, x, and its perimeter, y. The relationship is a direct variation because the equation $y = 5x$ is in the form $y = kx$, with $k = 5$.**

Coached Example

The graph on the right shows that the height of a
basketball's initial bounce varies directly as the
height from which the basketball is dropped.
Write an equation to represent this relationship.
Then predict the height of the initial bounce when
the basketball is dropped from a height of 100 inches.

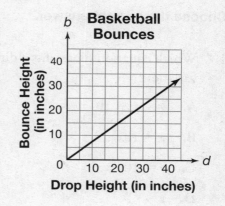

To find k, the constant of proportionality, solve the
equation for k.

On the graph, the independent variable is d and the
dependent variable is b. So use d for x and b for y.

$y = kx$

$b = kd$

$\dfrac{b}{d} = k$

Use a point on the graph, such as (40, _____). Substitute 40 for d and _____ for b.

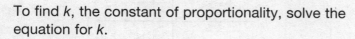

$\dfrac{b}{d} = k$

$\dfrac{\quad\quad}{40} = k$

$\underline{\quad\quad\quad} = k$

Substitute that value for k in the equation.

$b = kd = (\underline{\quad\quad})d$

The equation is $b = \underline{\quad\quad\quad}$.

Use the equation to find the height of the initial bounce if the basketball is dropped from
a height of 100 inches. Substitute 100 for d.

$b = (\underline{\quad\quad})d = (\underline{\quad\quad})(100) = \underline{\quad\quad}$

The equation for the direct variation is $b = \underline{\quad\quad\quad}$.

**Based on this equation, if a basketball is dropped from a height of 100 inches,
its initial bounce height will be about _____ inches.**

Choose the correct answer.

1. Which equation represents a direct variation?

   A. $y = x + 10$

   B. $y = 10x$

   C. $y = 10 - x$

   D. $y = \frac{10}{x}$

2. Which table represents a direct variation?

   A.

x	y
1	1
2	4
3	9
4	16

   B.

x	y
1	3
2	5
3	7
4	9

   C.

x	y
1	8
2	16
3	24
4	32

   D.

x	y
1	4
2	3
3	2
4	1

3. Which graph shows a direct variation?

   A.

   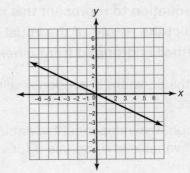

   B.

   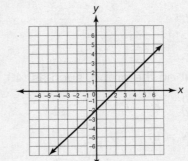

   C.

   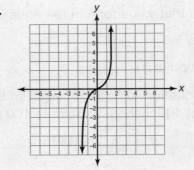

   D.

   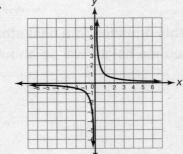

Use the graph for questions 4 and 5.

The graph below shows that the distance a grasshopper can jump, j, varies directly as the length of the grasshopper's body, b.

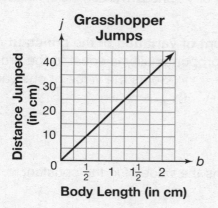

4. Which equation best represents the direct variation shown in the graph?

    A. $j = 0.1b$

    B. $j = 20b$

    C. $j = \dfrac{10}{b}$

    D. $j = \dfrac{20}{b}$

5. Based on the graph, if a grasshopper's body were 3 centimeters long, what distance would you expect it to jump?

    A. 30 centimeters

    B. 40 centimeters

    C. 50 centimeters

    D. 60 centimeters

6. Ron is on the track team. The table below shows that the distance in meters, d, Ron can run varies directly as the time, t, in minutes, that he runs.

t	0.5	1.5	2.5	3.5
d	100	300	500	700

Which equation represents this direct variation?

    A. $d = 3.5t$ **C.** $d = 400t$

    B. $d = 200t$ **D.** $d = 1{,}400t$

7. Drazen's weekly pay, p, in dollars, varies directly as the number of hours, h, that he works. If k is the constant of variation, which equation represents that situation?

    A. $p = h + k$

    B. $p = \dfrac{k}{h}$

    C. $p = \dfrac{h}{k}$

    D. $p = kh$

8. Which of the following represents a direct variation?

    A. The total cost, c, of a delivery of n sandwiches includes $6 for each sandwich plus a $5 delivery fee.

    B. Steliano's age, s, is 25 years less than Vincent's age, v.

    C. The total price, p, for tickets to a play is $18 times the number of tickets, t.

    D. The distance, in miles, d, of a train from its destination is the difference between 250 and 60 times h, the number of hours since its departure.

Inverse Variation

SOL: A.8

An **inverse variation** is a function in the form $y = \frac{k}{x}$, where k is a nonzero constant and $x \neq 0$. In this case, we say that y is inversely proportional to x, or y varies inversely as x. An inverse variation is also called an **indirect variation**.

Like direct variation, the constant k is called the **constant of variation** or the **constant** of **proportionality**. In an inverse relation, the constant of proportionality is equal to the product of the dependent variable and the independent variable ($k = xy$). So as the value of one variable increases, the value of the other decreases.

Example 1

If x varies inversely as y and if $x = 3$ when $y = 5$, what is the value of k, the constant of variation?

Strategy   **Substitute the given values into the equation for an inverse variation and solve for k.**

> **Step 1**   Substitute the given values into $y = \frac{k}{x}$.
> $$y = \frac{k}{x}$$
> $x = 3$ and $y = 5$
> $$5 = \frac{k}{3}$$

> **Step 2**   Solve for k.
> $$5 = \frac{k}{3}$$ Multiply both sides by 3.
> $$15 = k$$

Solution   **The constant of variation, k, is 15.**

Many real-world situations can be modeled by inverse variations. For example, the time to drive a certain distance varies inversely as the rate of travel (speed). As speed increases, the amount of time decreases.

Example 2

Latoya took $2\frac{1}{4}$ hours to drive to her cousin's house, driving at an average speed of 56 mph. Write an equation that represents the relationship between the speed at which Latoya drives and the time she takes to drive to her cousin's house.

Strategy   **Find k, the constant of variation. Then write the equation for the inverse variation.**

Step 1   Substitute the given values into the equation for an inverse variation.

Time (t) varies inversely as the rate of travel (r), so $t = \frac{k}{r}$.

Since the trip took $2\frac{1}{4}$ hours when Latoya drove at a rate of 56 mph,

$2\frac{1}{4} = \frac{k}{56}$.

Step 2   Solve the equation for k.

$2\frac{1}{4} = \frac{k}{56}$ Change the mixed number to a decimal.

$2.25 = \frac{k}{56}$ Multiply both sides by 56.

$126 = k$

Step 3   Write the equation that represents the inverse variation.

$t = \frac{k}{r}$

Since $k = 126$, the equation of the inverse variation is $t = \frac{126}{r}$.

Solution   **The equation for the inverse variation in this situation is $t = \frac{126}{r}$.**

Example 3

The table below shows the number of minutes different numbers of workers take to assemble an engine at a manufacturing plant. Does this data represent an indirect variation? If so, write an equation to represent the relationship.

Number of Workers (w)	Number of Minutes (m)
2	90
3	60
4	45

Strategy   **Find the product of w and m for each pair of values in the table. Then use the indirect variation formula to write an equation.**

Step 1   Find the product of w and m for each pair of values in the table.

In an indirect variation, $y = \frac{k}{x}$, so $k = xy$.

In this case, w is the independent variable and m is the dependent variable, so $k = wm$.

$2 \cdot 90 = 180$

$3 \cdot 60 = 180$

$4 \cdot 45 = 180$

The product is always equal to 180. So the data in the table represents an indirect variation.

Step 2   Write an equation to represent the relationship shown in the table.

The value of k, the constant of variation, is 180.

The formula for an indirect variation is $y = \frac{k}{x}$.

$$m = \frac{k}{w}$$

$$m = \frac{180}{w}$$

Solution   **The data represents an indirect variation and is described by the equation $m = \frac{180}{w}$.**

Coached Example

If x varies inversely as y and if $x = 4$ when $y = 12$, find x when $y = 6$.

The equation for an inverse variation is $y = $ _____.

What are the known paired values of x and y?

$x = $ _____; $y = $ _____

To find k, substitute the given pair of values for x and y into the equation.

_____

Solve the equation for k.

_____

$k = $ _____

Write the equation of the inverse variation using the variables x and y and the value you found for k. _____

Use your equation to find x when $y = 6$.

When $y = 6$, $x = $ _____.

Lesson Practice

Choose the correct answer.

1. Which equation represents an inverse variation?

   A. $y = 7x$

   B. $y = \frac{x}{7}$

   C. $y = x - 7$

   D. $y = \frac{7}{x}$

2. If x varies inversely as y and if $x = 3$ when $y = 12$, what is the value of k, the constant of variation?

   A. 4
   C. 15

   B. 9
   D. 36

3. If x varies inversely as y and if $x = {}^-30$ when $y = 5$, what is the value of y when $x = 6$?

   A. $^-36$
   C. 1

   B. $^-25$
   D. 25

4. The table below shows a relation.

x	1	2	3	4
y	24	12	8	6

   Which of the following is true of the relation?

   A. It is not an inverse variation.

   B. It is an inverse variation with $k = 6$.

   C. It is an inverse variation with $k = 24$.

   D. It is an inverse variation with $k = 25$.

5. A truck driver drove from one warehouse to another in 5 hours, traveling at an average speed of 42 mph. If the return trip took 6 hours, what was the driver's average speed on the return trip?

   A. 30 mph
   C. 38.5 mph

   B. 35 mph
   D. 50.4 mph

6. Six machines, each working at the same rate, take 40 minutes to fill 1,000 cans of tomatoes. How long would the same job take if two additional machines are used?

   A. 25 minutes
   C. 30 minutes

   B. 28 minutes
   D. 38 minutes

7. A candy store offers a choice of one of three different shapes of decorative containers for any 5-pound order of bulk candy. The base area and height of each container are shown in the table below.

Base Area in Square Inches (b)	Height in Inches (h)
25	8
40	5
50	4

   Which equation represents this indirect variation?

   A. $h = \frac{b}{5} + 3$
   C. $h = \frac{400}{b}$

   B. $h = \frac{200}{b}$
   D. $h = \frac{500}{b}$

Chapter 3 Review

1. The function $f(x) = {}^-3$ is shown in the graph below.

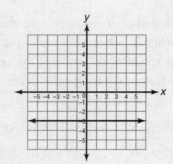

   What are the domain and range of this function?

   A. domain: $x = 0$;
      range: $f(x) = {}^-3$

   B. domain: all real numbers;
      range: $f(x) = {}^-3$

   C. domain: all real numbers;
      range: $f(x) \geq {}^-3$

   D. domain: all real numbers;
      range: all real numbers

2. Which table shows a relation that is **not** a function?

   A.
x	$^-2$	$^-1$	0	1	2
y	$^-8$	$^-1$	0	1	8

   B.
x	7	8	8	9	10
y	7	14	21	28	35

   C.
x	$^-8$	$^-4$	0	4	8
y	3	3	3	3	3

   D.
x	$^-10$	5	0	5	10
y	5	0	5	0	5

3. The number of minutes, m, Takashi takes to run five laps around the track varies inversely as his average speed, s, in meters per minute. If k is the constant of variation, what equation represents this situation?

   A. $m = s + k$

   B. $m = ks$

   C. $m = \frac{s}{k}$

   D. $m = \frac{k}{s}$

4. What are the zero(s) of the function $g(x) = x^2 - 36$?

   A. $^-36$

   B. 6

   C. $^-36$ and 0

   D. $^-6$ and 6

5. Which of the following graphs represents a function?

A.

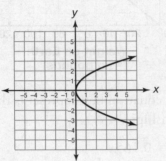

B.

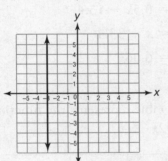

C.

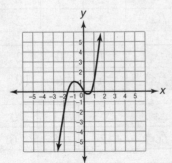

D.

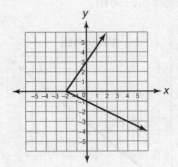

6. The function $f(x) = -x^2 - 2x + 2$ is shown below.

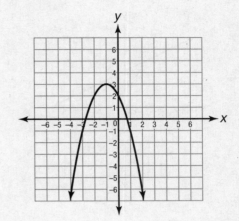

What is the y-intercept of this function?

A. -1

B. $\frac{2}{3}$

C. 2

D. 3

7. If $f(x) = x^2 - 2x + 8$, what is the value of $f(x)$ when $x = 5$?

A. 7

B. 8

C. 23

D. 36

8. What is the domain of the relation $\{(1, -2), (2, -4), (5, -7), (8, -12)\}$?

A. $\{1, 2, 5, 8\}$

B. $\{-4, -2, 1, 2\}$

C. $\{-12, -7, -4, -2\}$

D. $\{-12, -7, -4, -2, 1, 2, 5, 8\}$

9. Which function is represented by the graph below?

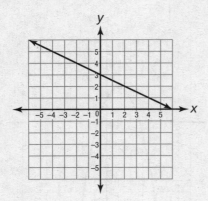

A. $f(x) = {}^-2x + 3$

B. $f(x) = {}^-\frac{3}{4}x + 3$

C. $f(x) = {}^-\frac{1}{2}x + 3$

D. $f(x) = 3x - 2$

10. What are the x- and y-intercepts of the function $f(x) = {}^-6x - 2$?

A. x-intercept: $\left({}^-\frac{1}{3}, 0\right)$,
   y-intercept: $(0, {}^-2)$

B. x-intercept: $({}^-2, 0)$,
   y-intercept: $\left(0, {}^-\frac{1}{3}\right)$

C. x-intercept: $({}^-2, 0)$,
   y-intercept: $\left(0, \frac{1}{3}\right)$

D. x-intercept: $\left(\frac{1}{3}, 0\right)$,
   y-intercept: $(0, {}^-2)$

11. The graph below shows that the weight of a person on the moon varies directly as his or her weight on Earth.

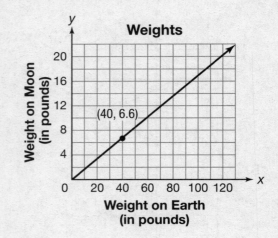

Which equation best represents this relationship?

A. $y = 0.165x$

B. $y = 0.5x - 13.4$

C. $y = x + 33.4$

D. $y = 6.06x$

12. Which table represents the function $f(x) = 2x^2 - 6$?

A.

x	-2	-1	2	3
$f(x)$	2	-4	2	12

B.

x	-1	0	2	3
$f(x)$	-4	-6	10	30

C.

x	-3	-1	0	1
$f(x)$	-24	-8	-6	-4

D.

x	-2	-1	1	3
$f(x)$	2	-8	-4	12

13. The table gives the cost for different numbers of 12-inch rulers. The cost, C, varies directly as the number of rulers, n.

Number of Rulers (n)	Cost in Dollars (C)
3	4.95
6	9.90
9	14.85
12	19.80

A. What is the constant of proportionality for this direct variation?

_____

B. Write an equation that represents the relationship shown in the table as a function $C(n)$.

_____

C. Using your function, find $C(5)$, the cost of 5 rulers. Show your work.

Chapter 4

Statistics

Mean Absolute Deviation

SOL: A.9

Statistics about a data set often describe measures of center, such as the arithmetic mean, and the dispersion, or spread, of the data. Recall that the arithmetic **mean** is equal to the sum of the elements divided by the total number of elements in the set. The Greek letter μ (mu) is used to represent the arithmetic mean of a data set.

One way to measure the variability of a data set is to measure the variation from the mean. For example, the two line plots below show the ages of volunteers at two different hospitals.

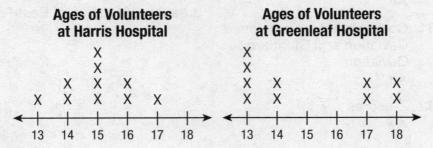

The mean age of volunteers for both hospitals is 15. However, the data for one of the plots varies more from the mean than the other plot.

You may be able to tell just by looking that the data for Greenleaf Hospital looks as if it varies more from the mean, 15, than the data for Harris Hospital. However, you can measure the exact amount of variation, or dispersion, by finding the **mean absolute deviation (MAD).**

$$\text{Mean absolute deviation} = \frac{\sum_{i=1}^{n} |x_i - \mu|}{n}, \text{ where } \mu \text{ represents the mean of}$$

the data set, n represents the number of elements in the data set, and x_i represents the ith element of the data set.

To find the MAD, first you must calculate the mean, μ. Next determine how much each data point varies, or deviates, from the mean by subtracting $x_i - \mu$. Then find the absolute values of those deviations from the mean. The reason we use absolute value is because without it, the sum of the deviations of data points from the mean of a data set is equal to 0, which does not help to describe the dispersion of the data set.

Finally, calculate the mean of the absolute values of those deviations to determine how much the data in the set varies from the mean.

The Σ symbol in the formula represents the sum of all values of the expression $|x_i - \mu|$ from $i = 1$ through $i = n$. When you divide the sum of all these absolute deviations by the number of elements, n, the result is the mean absolute deviation.

Example 1

The line plot on the right shows the ages of volunteers at Harris Hospital. The mean age of the volunteers is 15. Find the mean absolute deviation for the data.

Ages of Volunteers at Harris Hospital

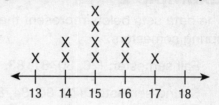

Strategy | **Subtract each age from the mean age, $\mu = 15$. Find the absolute values of those differences, and then find the mean of those values.**

Step 1 | Make a table to record your data.

Subtract 15 from each data point, x_1 through x_{10}, to find the deviation from the mean. Then take the absolute value of each of those deviations.

Age (x_i)	Deviation from Mean $(x_i - \mu)$	Absolute Deviation from Mean $(|x_i - \mu|)$
$x_1 = 13$	$13 - 15 = {}^-2$	$|{}^-2| = 2$
$x_2 = 14$	$14 - 15 = {}^-1$	$|{}^-1| = 1$
$x_3 = 14$	$14 - 15 = {}^-1$	$|{}^-1| = 1$
$x_4 = 15$	$15 - 15 = 0$	$|0| = 0$
$x_5 = 15$	$15 - 15 = 0$	$|0| = 0$
$x_6 = 15$	$15 - 15 = 0$	$|0| = 0$
$x_7 = 15$	$15 - 15 = 0$	$|0| = 0$
$x_8 = 16$	$16 - 15 = 1$	$|1| = 1$
$x_9 = 16$	$16 - 15 = 1$	$|1| = 1$
$x_{10} = 17$	$17 - 15 = 2$	$|2| = 2$

Step 2 | Find the mean absolute deviation.

Add the absolute deviations: $2 + 1 + 1 + 0 + 0 + 0 + 0 + 1 + 1 + 2 = 8$.

There are 10 data points in the set, so $n = 10$.

mean absolute deviation $= \frac{8}{10} = 0.8$

Solution | **The mean absolute deviation is 0.8 year.**

When the mean absolute deviation is small, as in Example 1, it means the data is bunched closely together. If the mean absolute deviation is large, it means the data is more spread out and has great variability.

You can also use a graphing calculator to calculate mean absolute deviation.

Example 2

The data sets below represent the grades Elton received in each of his classes in the fall and spring semesters.

Fall semester: {76, 80, 81, 83, 84, 88}

Spring semester: {79, 80, 84, 87, 91, 92}

Find and compare the mean absolute deviation for each of the semesters.

Strategy   **Use a graphing calculator to find each MAD.**

Step 1   Enter the data for both sets in the graphing calculator.

Press STAT and choose EDIT at the top of the screen.

Enter Elton's fall semester grades under L_1 and his spring semester grades under L_2.

L_1	L_2	L_3
76	79	----
80	80	
81	84	
83	87	
84	91	
88	92	
----	----	

Step 2   Use the calculator to determine the mean and MAD for set L_1.

Press STAT and choose the CALC menu. Select number 1: 1-Var Stats and enter L_1 by pressing 2nd 1 . Then press ENTER to view calculations for this list.

The value $\bar{x}$ represents the mean for this list. So the mean of Elton's fall semester grades is 82.

```
1-Var Stats
  x̄=82
  Σx=492
```

Next enter the formula for the MAD as "sum(abs($L_1 - \bar{x}$))/n." You can use CATALOG by pressing 2nd 0 to find "sum" and "abs." Press VARS and choose number 5: Statistics to find "$\bar{x}$" and "n."

Press ENTER . The screen shows a value of 3, which is the MAD for set L_1.

```
sum (abs (L₁−x̄))/n
                3
```

Step 3   Use the calculator to determine the mean and MAD
for set L_2.

> Press STAT and choose CALC, select
> 1: 1-Var Stats. Enter L_2 by pressing 2nd 2 .
>
> Press ENTER. The value of $\bar{x}$ is 85.5 for this set,
> so the mean of Elton's spring semester grades
> is 85.5.
>
> Again enter the MAD formula. This time, though,
> enter L_2 instead of L_1. Press ENTER. The screen
> shows a value of 4.5, which is the MAD for set L_2.

> 1-Var Stats
> $\bar{x} = 85.5$
> $\Sigma x = 513$

> sum (abs ($L_2 - \bar{x}$))/n
>   4.5

Solution   **The mean absolute deviation of Elton's spring semester grades, 4.5, is greater than the mean absolute deviation of his fall semester grades, 3.**

Coached Example

The line plot at the right shows the ages of volunteers at Greenleaf Hospital. Calculate the mean absolute deviation for the data. Which ages vary more from the mean—the ages of volunteers at Harris Hospital (see Example 1) or the ages of volunteers at Greenleaf Hospital?

Ages of Volunteers at Greenleaf Hospital

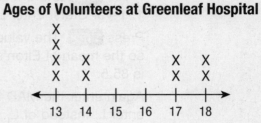

Complete the table below. Remember, the mean, or μ, is 15.

Age (x_i)	Deviation from Mean $(x_i - \mu)$	Absolute Deviation from Mean $(|x_i - \mu|)$
13	$13 - 15 = {}^-2$	$|{}^-2| = 2$
13		
13		
13		
14		
14		
17		
17		
18		
18		

Now find the mean of the absolute deviations.

Add the absolute deviations: _____

There are _____ data points in the set. So divide _____ by _____ to find the mean absolute deviation (MAD).

mean absolute deviation = _____

Example 1 showed that the MAD of ages of volunteers at Harris Hospital is _____ year(s).

The MAD of ages of volunteers at Greenleaf Hospital is _____ year(s).

Which mean absolute deviation is greater?

Since _____ year(s) > _____ year(s), the ages of volunteers at _____ Hospital vary more from the mean.

Lesson Practice

Choose the correct answer.

Use this line plot for questions 1 and 2.

This line plot shows the heights of 10 plants grown in a biology class.

Heights of Plants (in centimeters)

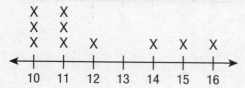

1. What is the mean height of the 10 plants?

   A. 12 centimeters

   B. 11.5 centimeters

   C. 11 centimeters

   D. 10.5 centimeters

2. What is the mean absolute deviation of the heights of the plants?

   A. 0 centimeters

   B. 0.8 centimeter

   C. 1 centimeter

   D. 1.8 centimeters

3. Below are the grades that Jim received on eight history quizzes.

   70, 80, 75, 80, 75, 85, 85, 90

   His mean quiz grade is an 80. What is the mean absolute deviation of his quiz grades?

   A. 0 points   **C.** 6 points

   B. 5 points   **D.** 40 points

4. This line plot shows the number of minutes that 10 piano students practice each day.

   Minutes Spent Practicing

   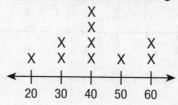

   The mean practice time is 41 minutes. What is the mean absolute deviation in practice times?

   A. 0 minutes

   B. 1.9 minutes

   C. 7.5 minutes

   D. 9.4 minutes

5. The table below gives the heights of five Virginia lighthouses.

Lighthouse	Tower Height (in feet)
Assateague Light	142
Cape Charles Light	191
Old Cape Henry Light	90
New Point Comfort Light	58
Old Point Comfort Light	54

   What is the mean absolute deviation of the heights of these five lighthouses?

   A. 10.7 feet

   B. 44.2 feet

   C. 47.6 feet

   D. 53.5 feet

Use the data in these line plots for questions 6–8.

The line plots below show the ages, in years, of 10 dogs at the vet's office on two different mornings last week.

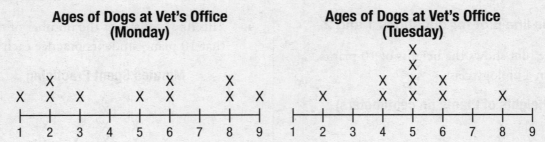

The mean age for both data sets is 5 years.

6. What was the mean absolute deviation of the ages of the dogs at the vet's office on Monday?

   A. 0.5 year

   B. 1.5 years

   C. 1.7 years

   D. 2.4 years

7. What was the mean absolute deviation of the ages of the dogs at the vet's office on Tuesday?

   A. 0.1 year

   B. 1 year

   C. 1.5 years

   D. 2.5 years

8. Which statement about the data sets is true?

   A. The data set for Monday is more variable than the data set for Tuesday.

   B. The data set for Monday is less variable than the data set for Tuesday.

   C. The variability for both data sets is about the same because the means of both data sets are the same.

   D. The variability for both data sets is about the same because the mean absolute deviations of both data sets are the same.

Variance and Standard Deviation

SOL: A.9

To describe how much a set of data varies from its mean statistically, you can use several different measures of variability. One measure of variability you have already learned about is mean absolute deviation. This measure uses absolute value to counteract the fact that some deviations from the mean will be positive and some will be negative. Another approach is to square each deviation, resulting in all positive numbers. The mean, or average, of the squared variations is a measure of variability called the **variance.** The symbol σ^2 represents the variance of a population, and the symbol S^2 represents the variance of a sample.

The formula for finding the variance of a population is shown below.

$$\text{Variance } (\sigma^2) = \frac{\sum_{i=1}^{n}(x_i - \mu)^2}{n},$$ where μ represents the mean of the data set, n represents the number of elements in the data set, and x_i represents the ith element of the data set.

When you have data for only a sample of the population and not the entire population, use the formula for S^2, which is the variance of a sample. Note that the denominator in this formula is $n - 1$ rather than n. This formula results in a slightly greater variance value to account for the possibility that data for the population varies more than what is seen in the sample.

$$\text{Variance of a sample } (S^2) = \frac{\sum_{i=1}^{n}(x_i - \overline{x})^2}{n - 1},$$ where $\overline{x}$ represents the mean of the sample data set, n represents the number of elements in the sample data set, and x_i represents the ith element of the sample data set.

Example 1

Students in Mr. Tyler's horticulture class grew bean plants. Ten plants were randomly selected. Their heights, in centimeters, were recorded below. Find the variance of the data for the horticulture class.

Plants Grown by Horticulture Class

Plant Heights (in centimeters)	10	14	11	12	10	13	13	12	13	12

Strategy   **Subtract each length from the mean length, and square the difference. Then use the correct formula to calculate the variance.**

Step 1   Identify which formula you should use.

The data includes only a sample of the heights of plants grown by students in the class. So use the formula for finding the variance of a sample.

Step 2   Find the mean plant height for the sample.

$$\frac{10 + 14 + 11 + 12 + 10 + 13 + 13 + 12 + 13 + 12}{10} = \frac{120}{10} = 12$$

Step 3   Identify what you need to do first, according to the formula.

First you need to calculate $\sum_{i=1}^{n} (x_i - \bar{x})^2$.

The expression $x_i - \bar{x}$ tells you to subtract the mean from each data point.

Then square each of those deviations: $(x_i - \bar{x})^2$

The symbol Σ tells you to find the sum of all those squared values.

Step 4   Find the sum of the squared deviations.

Data Value (x_i)	Deviation $(x_i - \bar{x})$	Square $(x_i - \bar{x})^2$
10	$10 - 12 = {}^-2$	$({}^-2)^2 = 4$
14	$14 - 12 = 2$	$(2)^2 = 4$
11	$11 - 12 = {}^-1$	$({}^-1)^2 = 1$
12	$12 - 12 = 0$	$(0)^2 = 0$
10	$10 - 12 = {}^-2$	$({}^-2)^2 = 4$
13	$13 - 12 = 1$	$(1)^2 = 1$
13	$13 - 12 = 1$	$(1)^2 = 1$
12	$12 - 12 = 0$	$(0)^2 = 0$
13	$13 - 12 = 1$	$(1)^2 = 1$
12	$12 - 12 = 0$	$(0)^2 = 0$

Find the sum of the squared deviations (the numbers in the last column):

$$\sum_{i=1}^{n} (x_i - \bar{x})^2 = 4 + 4 + 1 + 0 + 4 + 1 + 1 + 0 + 1 + 0 = 16$$

| Step 5 | Calculate the variance of the sample, using the formula. |

The sample size, n, is 10. You know that the sum of the squared deviations is 16.

$$S^2 = \frac{\sum\limits_{i=1}^{n}(x_i - \overline{x})^2}{n-1}$$

$$= \frac{16}{10-1}$$

$$= \frac{16}{9}$$

$$= 1.\overline{7}$$

Solution   **The variance is about 1.8 square centimeters.**

Variance is expressed in square units because it is the mean of the squares of the deviations. You can take the square root of the variance to find the **standard deviation,** another measure of variability in a data set. Standard deviation is expressed in the original units of measurement of the data. The symbol σ stands for the population standard deviation, and S stands for the sample standard deviation.

The formulas for finding standard deviations are shown below.

Sample Standard Deviation	Population Standard Deviation
$S = \sqrt{\dfrac{\sum\limits_{i=1}^{n}(x_i - \overline{x})^2}{n-1}}$	$\sigma = \sqrt{\dfrac{\sum\limits_{i=1}^{n}(x_i - \mu)^2}{n}}$

In these formulas, n represents the number of elements in the data set (sample or population, respectively), x_i is the ith element, $\overline{x}$ is the mean of the sample data set, and μ is the mean of the entire population data set.

Example 2

Find the standard deviation of the sample data for the horticulture class, shown below.

Plants Grown by Horticulture Class

Plant Heights (in centimeters)	10	14	11	12	10	13	13	12	13	12

Strategy **Use the appropriate standard deviation formula.**

Step 1 Identify which formula you should use.

The data includes only a sample of the heights of plants grown by students in the class. So use the formula for finding S, the sample standard deviation.

Step 2 Calculate the standard deviation, using the formula.

$$S = \sqrt{\frac{\sum\limits_{i=1}^{n}(x_i - \overline{x})^2}{n - 1}}$$

The expression under the radical symbol represents the variance of the sample.

In Example 1, you found the variance of this sample data set, which is equal to $1.\overline{7}$, or $\frac{16}{9}$.

Substitute the variance value for the variance expression in the formula, and simplify.

$$S = \sqrt{\frac{16}{9}}$$

$$= \frac{\sqrt{16}}{\sqrt{9}}$$

$$= \frac{4}{3}$$

$$= 1.\overline{3}$$

Solution **The standard deviation is about 1.3 centimeters.**

Standard deviation expresses the amount of dispersion about the mean. Low standard deviations, like the one in Example 2, indicate that data are clustered together. High standard deviations indicate that data are more spread out and have greater variability.

You can also use a graphing calculator to find the standard deviation for a data set.

Example 3

Students in Mr. Tyler's biology class also grew bean plants. Ten plants were randomly selected. Their heights, in centimeters, were recorded below. Find the standard deviation for the data for the biology class.

Plants Grown by Biology Class

Plant Heights (in centimeters)	8	15	10	8	16	16	10	14	9	14

Strategy   **Use a graphing calculator.**

Step 1   Enter the data into the calculator.

Press STAT and select 1: Edit.

This brings up three columns for listing data. Enter the data for the class in list L_1.

L_1	L_2	L_3
8	--------	--------
15		
10		
8		
16		
16		
10		

Step 2   Find the standard deviation.

Press STAT .

Press ▷ to move to the CALC menu.

Then select 1: 1–Var Stats and press 2nd , 1 , and ENTER since the list is in L_1.

```
1-Var Stats
 x̄=12
 Σx=120
 Σx²=1538
 Sx=3.299831646
 σx=3.130495168
↓n=10
■
```

The data includes only a sample of the lengths of plants grown by students in the biology class. So use the sample standard deviation, S, not the population standard deviation, σ.

The standard deviation is about 3.3 centimeters.

Solution   **The standard deviation is about 3.3 centimeters.**

The standard deviation for the biology class data set (3.3) is greater than the standard deviation for the horticulture class data set (1.3). Even though both samples have the same mean height, 12 centimeters, the sample from the biology class is more variable than the sample from the horticulture class.

Coached Example

The ages of all 7 members of a running club are: 18, 17, 18, 21, 20, 17, 22. The mean age of the runners is 19. Find the standard deviation.

Since the population is all the members of the running club, you need to find the population standard deviation.

Complete the table below.

Data Value (x_i)	18	17	18	21	20	17	22
Data Value − Mean ($x_i - \mu$)							
Square ($x_i - \mu$)^2							

Now add the squares.

$\sum_{i=1}^{n} (x_i - \mu)^2 = $ _____ + _____ + _____ + _____ + _____ + _____ + _____ = _____

There are _____ members in the club, so $n = $ _____.

The mean, μ, is given as 19.

Substitute those values into the formula and solve. Round your answer to the nearest hundredth.

$$\sigma = \sqrt{\frac{\sum_{i=1}^{n} (x_i - \mu)^2}{n}}$$

$$\sigma = \sqrt{\rule{3cm}{0pt}} \approx = \underline{\hspace{2cm}}$$

Use your graphing calculator to check your answer.

List the data by entering it in list L_1, as you did in Example 3. (If data are already in that column, move your cursor up to L1 and hit CLEAR to clear the list.)

Then press STAT , move to the CALC menu, and select 1: 1–Var Stats. Press 2nd and 1 since the list is in L_1.

Read the population standard deviation. Does it match the value of σ you found above? _____

The standard deviation of the ages is approximately _____ years.

The standard deviation of the ages is approximately _____ years.

Lesson Practice

Choose the correct answer.

Use this line plot for questions 1–3.

This line plot shows the ages of a sample of dancers in a contest.

Ages of a Sample of Dancers

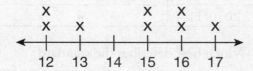

1. What is the mean age of the dancers?

   A. 11.6 years

   B. 13.5 years

   C. 14 years

   D. 14.5 years

2. What is the approximate variance of the dancers' ages?

   A. 1.35 years^2

   B. 3.25 years^2

   C. 3.71 years^2

   D. 3.9 years^2

3. What is the approximate standard deviation of the dancers' ages?

   A. 1.16 years

   B. 1.45 years

   C. 1.71 years

   D. 1.93 years

Use these data for questions 4 and 5.

The table below shows the heights, in inches, of samples of players taken from two basketball teams.

Heights of Players (in inches)

Eagles	68	70	72	72	73
Falcons	65	66	72	73	74

4. Which best describes the sample standard deviation for the Falcons?

   A. 2 inches

   B. 3.74 inches

   C. 4.18 inches

   D. 7 inches

5. Which statement accurately compares the data?

   A. The mean height is the same for both teams.

   B. The mean height is greater for the Falcons than for the Eagles.

   C. The sample standard deviation is the same for both teams.

   D. The data set for the Falcons is more variable than the data set for the Eagles.

6. The record high temperatures for Virginia and its five bordering states are given in the table below.

State	Record High Temperature (in degrees Celsius)
Kentucky	46
Maryland	43
North Carolina	43
Tennessee	45
Virginia	43
West Virginia	44

Which value represents the variance of the record high temperatures of these six states?

A. 1   C. 1.5

B. $1.\overline{3}$ D. 2

7. The table below shows the number of wins per season for the University of Virginia Cavaliers, for six consecutive seasons.

Season	Number of Games Won
2005/06	7
2006/07	5
2007/08	9
2008/09	5
2009/10	3
2010/11	4

Which best describes the standard deviation for the Cavaliers' number of wins per season for these six seasons?

A. $1.\overline{6}$ games   C. 4 games

B. 2 games   D. 5.5 games

8. Ms. Moro wants to compare the history quiz scores of students in her 1st-period class to those of students in her 2nd- and 3rd-period classes. The scores of ten students from each class were selected at random and are listed below.

1st Period	2nd Period	3rd Period
100	75	90
80	85	95
95	80	70
90	85	85
100	90	95
70	70	95
75	75	100
76	85	95
85	85	90
90	90	90

Which is **not** true of the variability of the sample data?

A. The standard deviation for the 2nd-period class was about 6.7 points.

B. The standard deviation for the 3rd-period class was about 8.3 points.

C. The sample from the 1st-period class was the most variable of all the samples.

D. The sample from the 3rd-period class was the least variable of all the samples.

Compare Mean Absolute Deviation and Standard Deviation

SOL: A.9

Variance, standard deviation, and mean absolute deviation each measure the dispersion of a set of data. Standard deviation and mean absolute deviation are both expressed in the original units of measurement of the data. However, the standard deviation and mean absolute deviation (MAD) may be less similar for some sets of data than for others.

Example 1

Meg and Eric each recorded the number of hours she or he slept each night for ten nights. Line plots for each set of data are shown below, as well as the mean, variance, standard deviation, and mean absolute deviation for each set of data. (Values are rounded to the nearest tenth.) Compare and contrast the standard deviation and mean absolute deviation for these two data sets.

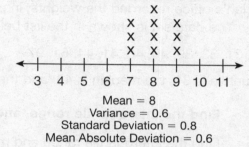

Meg's Hours of Sleep per Night

Mean = 7
Variance = 5.8
Standard Deviation = 2.4
Mean Absolute Deviation = 2.2

Eric's Hours of Sleep per Night

Mean = 8
Variance = 0.6
Standard Deviation = 0.8
Mean Absolute Deviation = 0.6

Strategy Compare and contrast the given measures of standard deviation and MAD.

Step 1 Compare the standard deviation and MAD for the two sets of data.

The standard deviation for Meg's data set, 2.4 hours, is greater than the standard deviation for Eric's data set, 0.8 hour.

The MAD for Meg's data set, 2.2 hours, is greater than the MAD for Eric's data set, 0.6 hour.

So both the standard deviation and the MAD are greater for Meg's data set than for Eric's data set. These differences represent a greater dispersion of data in Meg's data set than in Eric's data set.

Step 2 Contrast the standard deviation and MAD for the two sets of data.

The standard deviation is greater than the MAD for each of the sets of data (2.4 > 2.2 and 0.8 > 0.6).

Find the difference between the standard deviation and MAD for each data set.

Meg's data set: 2.4 − 2.2 = 0.2

Eric's data set: 0.8 − 0.6 = 0.2

The difference for both sets of data is 0.2.

Solution	Both the standard deviation and the MAD are greater for Meg's data set than for Eric's data set. The difference between the standard deviation and the mean absolute deviation is the same for both sets of data.

The **median** of a data set is the middle term, or the average of the two middle terms, when the terms are arranged from least to greatest. When data are arranged from least to greatest, the **lower quartile**, or **first quartile**, is the median of the lower half of the data. The **upper quartile**, or **third quartile**, is the median of the upper half of the data.

The variance and standard deviation are more affected than the mean absolute deviation by **outliers** within the data set. Outliers are elements that fall at least 1.5 times the interquartile range below the first quartile (Q_1) or above the third quartile (Q_3). The **interquartile range** (IQR) is the difference between the third and first quartiles: $Q_3 - Q_1$. To identify quartiles and outliers, you may want to arrange the elements in a data set from least to greatest.

Example 2

A veterinarian's office recorded the weights, in pounds, of all of the dogs that had appointments on Monday. The data set is shown in the list below.

13, 16, 31, 33, 39, 40, 40, 41, 44, 61, 97

The first quartile is 31, the median is 40, and the third quartile is 44. Are there any outliers?

Strategy	Find the interquartile range, and use it to find any outliers.
Step 1	Find the interquartile range and multiply it by 1.5.
	Outliers are elements that fall at least 1.5 times the interquartile range below the first quartile or above the third quartile.
	The IQR is the difference between the third quartile and the first quartile.
	$44 - 31 = 13$
	Find 1.5 times the interquartile range: $1.5 \times 13 = 19.5$
Step 2	Look for outliers below the first quartile.
	Subtract 1.5 times the IQR from the first quartile.
	$31 - 19.5 = 11.5$
	The least number in the set, 13, is greater than 11.5. So there are no outliers below the first quartile.
Step 3	Look for outliers above the third quartile.
	Add 1.5 times the IQR to the third quartile.
	$44 + 19.5 = 63.5$
	The greatest number in the set, 97, is greater than 63.5. So 97 is an outlier.
Solution	The set has one outlier, 97 pounds.

Example 3

Mr. Pace owns ten turtles. Their ages, in years, are listed in the table below.

Age (in years)	2	2	2	2	3	3	4	6	6	20

The mean age for a turtle in this group is 5 years; the mean absolute deviation is 3.4 years; and the standard deviation is about 5.2 years. Which is a better measure to use to describe the dispersion in this data set, the MAD or the standard deviation?

Strategy **Compare the turtles' ages to the mean. Compare the MAD and standard deviation to these values.**

Step 1 Find the deviations from the mean for each element.

The mean age is 5 years.

$2 - 5 = {}^{-}3$

$2 - 5 = {}^{-}3$

$2 - 5 = {}^{-}3$

$2 - 5 = {}^{-}3$

$3 - 5 = {}^{-}2$

$3 - 5 = {}^{-}2$

$4 - 5 = {}^{-}1$

$6 - 5 = 1$

$6 - 5 = 1$

$20 - 5 = 15$

Four turtles are 3 years younger than the mean, two turtles are 2 years younger, one turtle is 1 year younger, two turtles are 1 year older, and one turtle is 15 years older.

Step 2 Compare the MAD and standard deviation values to the set of deviations.

A measure of dispersion represents how the data points in a set vary from the mean.

The MAD is about 3.4 years, and the standard deviation is about 5.2 years.

Each turtle's age, with the exception of the outlier, is within 3 years of the mean age.

So the MAD better represents the dispersion of data than the standard deviation.

Solution **The mean absolute deviation better describes the dispersion in this data set than the standard deviation.**

Coached Example

Mrs. Garcia counted the number of customers who entered her shop each day for two weeks in January and for two weeks in June. She graphed the data in histograms and also calculated the mean, mean absolute deviation, and standard deviation for each data set, as shown below.

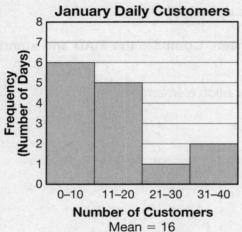

January Daily Customers
Mean = 16
Mean Absolute Deviation = 7.7
Standard Deviation = 10.0

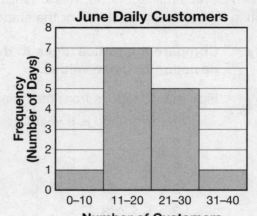

June Daily Customers
Mean = 20
Mean Absolute Deviation = 6.4
Standard Deviation = 7.7

Compare and contrast the mean absolute deviation and standard deviation for these two data sets.

The mean absolute deviation was greater for _____ than for _____.

The standard deviation was greater for _____ than for _____.

This means that greater variability occurred in the data for _____ than for _____.

For January, the _____ deviation was greater than the _____ deviation.

For June, the _____ deviation was greater than the _____ deviation.

The mean absolute deviation and standard deviation were closer in value for _____ than for _____.

The mean absolute deviation and standard deviation were both greater for _____ than for _____. For both data sets, the _____ deviation was greater than the _____ deviation. However, they were more similar for _____ than for _____.

Lesson Practice

Choose the correct answer.

Use the information below for questions 1–3.

The Dyer family went shopping for clothing and bought ten items with the following prices.

$18, $24, $25, $25, $5, $27, $18, $26, $50, $22

For this data set, the mean is $24, the first quartile is $18, and the third quartile is $26. The mean absolute deviation is 6.6, and the standard deviation is 10.6.

1. What are the outlier(s), if any?

    A. There are no outliers.

    B. There is exactly one outlier, $5.

    C. There is exactly one outlier, $50.

    D. There are exactly two outliers, $5 and $50.

2. Which measure best represents the dispersion of this data set?

    A. mean absolute deviation

    B. standard deviation

    C. variance

    D. interquartile range

3. How would the removal of the minimum value and maximum value from the set affect the mean absolute deviation and standard deviation of the set?

    A. The MAD and standard deviation would become equal.

    B. The MAD would become greater than the standard deviation.

    C. The MAD and standard deviation would become closer together in value.

    D. The MAD and standard deviation would become further apart in value.

4. For which of the following data sets is the mean absolute value most likely to be a much better measure of dispersion than the standard deviation?

    A. {8, 8, 8, 8, 8, 8, 8, 8, 8}

    B. {10, 12, 12, 14, 15, 15, 15, 16, 19}

    C. {4, 15, 19, 19, 20, 20, 21, 23, 25}

    D. {1, 1, 3, 4, 4, 5, 5, 6, 9}

Use the information below for questions 5 and 6.

Etienne's soccer team scored the following numbers of points in their first 12 games.

Game Number	1	2	3	4	5	6	7	8	9	10	11	12
Number of Points	7	1	0	3	2	3	5	4	4	1	4	2

They have scored a mean of 3 points per game during these games, with a mean absolute deviation of 1.5 points.

5. Which of the following is a likely conclusion regarding the standard deviation?

   A. The standard deviation should be equal to the mean absolute deviation.

   B. The standard deviation should be less than the mean absolute deviation.

   C. The standard deviation should be greater than the mean absolute deviation.

   D. The standard deviation should be greater than the variance.

6. If Etienne's team scores 7 points in their 13th game, which of the following should result for the data set of all 13 games, as compared with the data set for the first 12 games?

   A. The MAD and standard deviation will remain the same.

   B. The MAD and standard deviation will both increase.

   C. The MAD and standard deviation will both decrease.

   D. The MAD will decrease, and the standard deviation will increase.

Z-scores

SOL: A.9

The **z-score** associated with a data value measures the number of standard deviations the data value lies above or below the mean. It is positive if the data value is greater than the mean and negative if the data value is less than the mean. For example, a data value with a z-score of 1.5 lies 1.5 standard deviations above the mean. A data value with a z-score of $^-0.6$ lies 0.6 standard deviation below the mean. The formula for calculating z-scores, which are also called standard scores, is given below.

> If x represents a data value from a data set with mean μ and standard deviation σ, then
> $$z = \frac{x - \mu}{\sigma}.$$

Example 1

A researcher is studying the amount of time high school students take to complete a test. The data collected for the study produced a mean of 80 minutes and a standard deviation of 8 minutes. What is the z-score for a time of 90 minutes, and what does this represent?

Strategy   Use the formula for finding a z-score. Use the definition of z-score to interpret what the z-score means.

Step 1   Use the formula for finding a z-score.

Substitute 90 for x, 80 for μ, and 8 for σ.

$$z = \frac{x - \mu}{\sigma}$$

$$z = \frac{90 - 80}{8}$$

$$z = \frac{10}{8}$$

$$z = 1.25$$

Step 2   Interpret the meaning of the z-score.

A z-score tells how many standard deviations the data value is above or below the mean. A positive z-score lies above the mean.

The z-score for 90 is positive 1.25. So a value of 90 lies 1.25 standard deviations above the mean of 80 minutes. In other words, a time of 90 minutes is 1.25 times the standard deviation of 8 minutes above the mean of 80 minutes.

Solution   **The z-score for 90 minutes is 1.25. This means that a time of 90 minutes is 1.25 standard deviations above the mean time for finishing the test.**

If you are given the mean and standard deviation for a data set and the z-score for an unknown element in the set, you can calculate the value of the element.

Example 2

The line plot below shows the quiz scores of the 15 students in Mr. Wagner's math class. The mean quiz score is 82, and the standard deviation is 8 points.

Quiz Scores

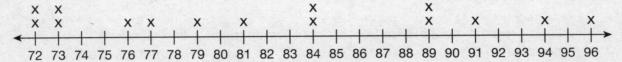

Which quiz score represents a z-score of $^-1.25$? How many students scored within one standard deviation of the mean?

Strategy   **Use the definition of z-score to find the unknown quiz score. Calculate the quiz scores one standard deviation above and below the mean. Count the number of elements in between.**

Step 1   Find the quiz score with a z-score of $^-1.25$.

The z-score represents the number of standard deviations the data value is above or below the mean. A quiz score with a z-score of $^-1.25$ lies 1.25 standard deviations below the mean.

The mean is 82, and the standard deviation is 8.

Multiply the z-score by the standard deviation, and add this value to the mean.

$82 + (^-1.25)(8) = 82 - 10 = 72$

The quiz score of 72 has a z-score of $^-1.25$.

Step 2   Find the number of students who scored within one standard deviation of the mean.

Subtract the standard deviation, 8, from the mean, 82, to find the data value one standard deviation below the mean.

$\mu - \sigma = 82 - 8 = 74$

Add the standard deviation, 8, to the mean, 82, to find the data value one standard deviation above the mean.

$\mu + \sigma = 82 + 8 = 90$

Eight data points on the line plot are between 74 and 90: 76, 77, 79, 81, 84, 84, 89, and 89.

So 8 students scored within one standard deviation of the mean.

Solution   **The quiz score of 72 represents a z-score of $^-1.25$. Eight students scored within one standard deviation of the mean.**

Coached Example

The data in this graph show the amount of time students spend riding the bus to school. The mean commute time is 14 minutes, and the standard deviation is 2 minutes.

What is the z-score for an 11-minute commute? Which commute time has a z-score of 3?

Students' Bus Rides

Length of Bus Ride (in minutes)

The formula for calculating a z-score is $z =$ _____, where x represents the element in the data set, μ represents the mean of the data set, and σ represents the standard deviation of the data set.

To find the z-score for an 11-minute commute, substitute _____ for x, _____ for μ, and _____ for σ.

Calculate the z-score for an 11-minute commute.

An 11-minute commute has a z-score of _____. The z-score is _____ because the value lies below the mean.

A commute time with a z-score of 3 lies _____ standard deviations _____ the mean.

Calculate the value of the element with a z-score of 3.

So the commute time with a z-score of 3 is _____ minutes.

An 11-minute commute has a z-score of _____. The commute time of _____ minutes has a z-score of 3.

Lesson Practice

Choose the correct answer.

1. If a data set has a mean of 150 and a standard deviation of 25, what is the z-score of an element with a value of 250?

   A. $1.\overline{6}$

   B. 4

   C. 6

   D. 10

2. If the mean of a set of data is 23 and the standard deviation is 4, what data value has a z-score of $^-1.5$?

   A. 17

   B. 17.5

   C. 18.5

   D. 21.5

3. If a data set has a mean of 8.4 and a standard deviation of 2.2, what interval includes all values within two standard deviations of the mean?

   A. $0 \leq x \leq 16.8$

   B. $1.8 \leq x \leq 15.0$

   C. $4.0 \leq x \leq 12.8$

   D. $6.2 \leq x \leq 10.6$

Use the following information for questions 4 and 5.

Data collected for a study involving IQ scores of 5-year-old girls produced a mean of 100 and a standard deviation of 15.

4. What is the z-score associated with an IQ of 112?

   A. 1.25

   B. 0.8

   C. 0.6

   D. 0.12

5. What does a z-score of $^-2$ represent?

   A. an IQ that is 2 points below the mean

   B. an IQ that is 2 points above the mean

   C. an IQ that is 2 standard deviations below the mean

   D. an IQ that is 2 standard deviations above the mean

Use the line plot and information below for questions 6–8.

A group of eight friends went to the Busch Gardens theme park in Williamsburg. The line plot below represents the number of rides each friend went on. The mean is 11 rides, and the standard deviation is 2.5.

Number of Rides per Person

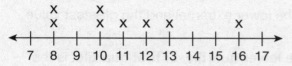

6. Which number of rides has a z-score of 2?

   A. 8

   B. 12

   C. 13

   D. 16

7. Diane is one of the two people in the group who went on 10 rides. Which z-score represents 10 rides in this data set?

   A. ⁻4

   B. ⁻1

   C. ⁻0.4

   D. 4

8. A z-score of 0 represents the number of rides Sam went on. How many rides did Sam go on?

   A. 0

   B. 8

   C. 10

   D. 11

Box-and-Whisker Plots

SOL: A.10

A **box-and-whisker plot** is a good way to show the spread (or variation) of a set of data visually. A box-and-whisker plot sits above and/or below a number line. The values for the plot are read from the number line.

A box-and-whisker plot shows both the median and the **extremes** of a data set. The **median** of a data set is the middle term, or the average of the two middle terms, when the terms are arranged from least to greatest.

Range is the difference between the least value (the lower extreme) and the greatest value (the upper extreme) in a data set.

When data are arranged from least to greatest, the **lower quartile**, or **first quartile**, is the median of the lower half of the data. The **upper quartile**, or **third quartile**, is the median of the upper half of the data.

Together, the lower quartile, median, and upper quartile divide the full set of data into four smaller sets of data. The **interquartile range** is the difference between the upper quartile and the lower quartile.

The diagram below shows how to read a box-and-whisker plot.

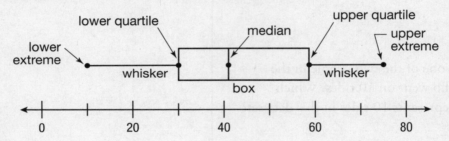

Example 1

Mr. Patterson surveyed members of the school band and members of the school orchestra to find out how many CDs each owned. His data is shown in the box-and-whisker plots on the right. Compare the medians of the two sets.

CDs Owned by Band and Orchestra Members

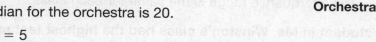

Strategy   **Read the box-and-whisker plots. Then compare.**

The median for the band is 25.
The median for the orchestra is 20.

$25 - 20 = 5$

The median for the band members is 5 more than for the orchestra members.

Solution   **The median number of CDs owned by band members is 5 more than the median number of CDs owned by orchestra members.**

Example 2

The double box-and-whisker plot below shows the test scores for two classes.

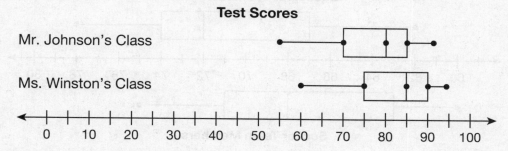

Which class has the student with the highest test score? Which class has the greater interquartile range?

Strategy   **Find the upper extreme and interquartile range for each plot.**

Step 1   To find the highest test score, find the upper extreme of each plot.

In a box-and-whisker plot, the upper extreme is at the far right end of the whisker on the right.

Mr. Johnson's Class: about 92

Ms. Winston's Class: about 94

$94 > 92$

Ms. Winston's class has the student with the highest test score.

Step 2	Find the interquartile range for each plot.

The interquartile range is the difference between the upper and lower quartiles.

In a box-and-whisker plot, the upper quartile is shown by the right edge of the box. The lower quartile is shown by the left edge of the box.

Mr. Johnson's class: The lower quartile is 70. The upper quartile is 85.

Interquartile range: $85 - 70 = 15$

Ms. Winston's class: The lower quartile is 75. The upper quartile is 90.

Interquartile range: $90 - 75 = 15$

$15 = 15$

The interquartile range is the same for each class.

Solution **A student in Ms. Winston's class had the highest test score. The interquartile ranges of the two classes are equal.**

Example 3

The double box-and-whisker plot below represents the heights, in inches, of the basketball and soccer team members.

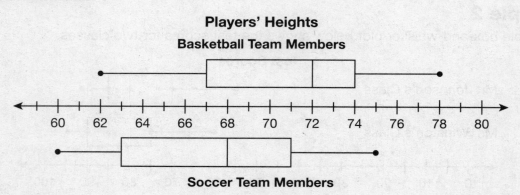

Players' Heights

Basketball Team Members

Soccer Team Members

Which team has the shortest player? Which team has a greater range of player heights?

Strategy **Find the lower extreme and the range for each plot.**

Step 1	To find the shortest height, find the lower extreme of each plot.

The lower extreme is at the far left end of the whisker on the left.

Basketball team members: 62

Soccer team members: 60

$60 < 62$

The soccer team has the shortest player, who is 60 inches tall.

Step 2   Find the range for each plot.

The range is the difference between the maximum and minimum values in the set, or the upper and lower extremes.

Basketball team members: The lower extreme is 62. The upper extreme is 78.

Range: $78 - 62 = 16$

Soccer team members: The lower extreme is 60. The upper extreme is 75.

Range: $75 - 60 = 15$

$16 > 15$

The basketball team has a greater range of player heights.

Solution   **A member of the soccer team is the shortest player. The basketball team has a greater range of player heights.**

Coached Example

Ninth-grade athletes at Terrell High School sold energy bars for a fundraiser. Imani surveyed 10 male athletes and 10 female athletes to find out how many energy bars each group had sold. The double box-and-whisker plot displays the results of Imani's survey.

Number of Energy Bars Sold

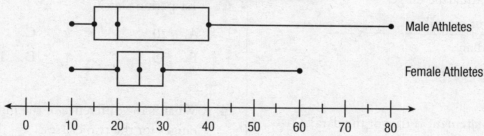

Male Athletes

Female Athletes

Which group had the greater median? How much greater was it?

In a box-and-whisker plot, the median is marked by the line inside the box.

The median for the male athletes is _____.

The median for the female athletes is _____.

The _____ athletes had the greater median.

The difference between the two medians is _____ − _____ = _____.

The median number sold was _____ more for the _____ athletes than for the _____ athletes.

Lesson Practice

Choose the correct answer.

Use the information and the box-and-whisker plots below for questions 1 and 2.

These plots show bowling scores for samples drawn from two different leagues.

Bowling Scores

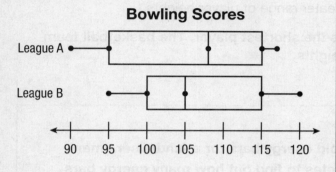

1. Which measure is the same for both samples?

    A. interquartile range

    B. lower quartile

    C. median

    D. upper quartile

2. Which statement is true of the data?

    A. League A had the highest bowling score.

    B. League B had a greater median score.

    C. League A had a greater range of scores.

    D. League B had a greater interquartile range of scores.

Use the information and the box-and-whisker plots below for questions 3–5.

Mr. Smith gave the same math test to his 1st- and 2nd-period classes. These box-and-whisker plots show how the students from each class scored on the test.

Test Scores

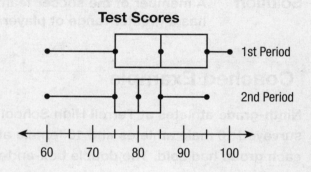

3. What is the range of test scores for the 1st-period class?

    A. 20   C. 40

    B. 35   D. 100

4. What is the difference of the interquartile ranges for the two classes?

    A. 10   C. 20

    B. 15   D. 25

5. Which of the following are the same for both classes?

    A. lower extreme and range

    B. lower extreme and lower quartile

    C. median and upper quartile

    D. upper quartile and upper extreme

Use the information and the box-and-whisker plots below for questions 6–8.

Jenelle recorded the length, in minutes, of each movie in her collection. These box-and-whisker plots show the data for the comedies and dramas.

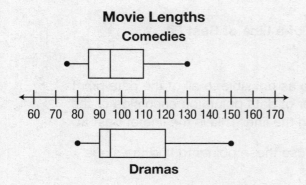

Movie Lengths

6. Which measure is the same for both the comedies and the dramas?

   A. lower extreme

   B. lower quartile

   C. upper quartile

   D. median

7. Which of the following describes the shortest and longest movies in Jenelle's collection?

   A. The shortest and longest movies are both comedies.

   B. The shortest and longest movies are both dramas.

   C. The shortest movie is a comedy, and the longest movie is a drama.

   D. The shortest movie is a drama, and the longest movie is a comedy.

8. Which statement describes the difference in interquartile ranges?

   A. The interquartile range for dramas is the same as the interquartile range for comedies.

   B. The interquartile range for dramas is approximately 5 minutes longer than the interquartile range for comedies.

   C. The interquartile range for dramas is approximately 10 minutes longer than the interquartile range for comedies.

   D. The interquartile range for dramas is approximately 15 minutes longer than the interquartile range for comedies.

Line of Best Fit

SOL: A.11

When a scatterplot shows a trend in the data displayed, a line can be drawn that passes through or is close to most of the points in the scatterplot. This line is called a **line of best fit**. You can find an equation for the line of best fit for a set of data by following the steps below. The process of finding the line of best fit is called **linear regression**.

> ### Writing the Equation of a Line of Best Fit
>
> 1. Graph the data points in a scatterplot.
>
> 2. Draw a straight line that lies as close as possible to all of the data points, with approximately the same number of data points on each side of the line and some data points directly on the line. This is the line of best fit.
>
> 3. Identify two points on that line, and use those points to find the slope. The equation for slope is $m = \frac{y_2 - y_1}{x_2 - x_1}$.
>
> 4. Substitute the slope, m, and the coordinates of one point on the line (x_1, y_1) into the point-slope form, $y - y_1 = m(x - x_1)$. Simplify to get the equation for the line of best fit into slope-intercept form, $y = mx + b$.

Example 1

The graph below shows the heights and shoe sizes of 20 girls.

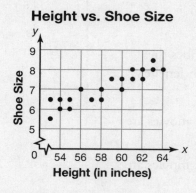

Height vs. Shoe Size

Write an equation for the line of best fit for these data.

Strategy   Draw a line of best fit. Then use the slope and a point to write the equation of the line.

Step 1   Draw a line of best fit.

Draw a line that passes through or is close to as many points as possible.

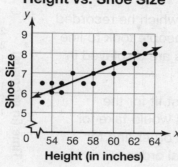

Height vs. Shoe Size

Step 2   Find the slope.

The points (58, 7) and (63, 8) lie on the line of best fit.

$$m = \frac{y_2 - y_1}{x_2 - x_1} = \frac{8 - 7}{63 - 58} = \frac{1}{5}$$

Step 3   Write the equation of the line.

Use the slope, $\frac{1}{5}$, and the point (63, 8) in the point-slope form of a linear equation.

$$y - y_1 = m(x - x_1)$$

$$y - 8 = \frac{1}{5}(x - 63)$$

$$y - 8 = \frac{1}{5}x - 12\frac{3}{5}$$

$$y = \frac{1}{5}x - 4\frac{3}{5}$$

Solution   The equation of the line of best fit is $y = \frac{1}{5}x - 4\frac{3}{5}$.

The equation of a line of best fit can help you make predictions from the data in a scatterplot.

Example 2

Omar conducted an experiment in which he recorded the number of seconds groups of people took to line up in alphabetical order. His results are displayed in the scatterplot to the right.

Write an equation for the line of best fit for the scatterplot. Then predict the time it would take for 18 people to line up in alphabetical order and for 100 people to line up in alphabetical order.

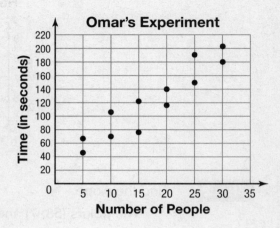

Strategy	Draw a line of best fit and find its equation. Then use the equation to make predictions.

Step 1   Draw a line of best fit.

Step 2   Use the coordinates of two points on the line to find the slope.

Use (10, 70) and (20, 140) to find the slope.

$$m = \frac{y_2 - y_1}{x_2 - x_1} = \frac{140 - 70}{20 - 10} = \frac{70}{10} = 7$$

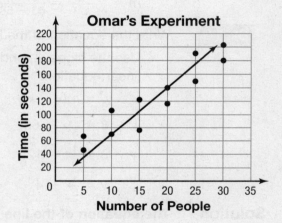

Step 3   Substitute the value of the slope and the coordinates of one of the points in the point-slope form.

Use (10, 70).

$$y - y_1 = m(x - x_1)$$
$$y - 70 = 7(x - 10)$$

Step 4   Rewrite the equation in slope-intercept form.

$$y - 70 = 7(x - 10)$$
$$y - 70 = 7x - 70$$
$$y = 7x$$

Step 5   Use the equation to make predictions.

For 18 people: $y = 7x = 7(18) = 126$

For 100 people: $y = 7x = 7(100) = 700$

Solution   **The equation of the line of best fit is $y = 7x$. It will take 18 people about 126 seconds to line up in alphabetical order. It will take 100 people about 700 seconds to line up in alphabetical order.**

The equation of the line of best fit depends on how you choose to draw the line. So equations might vary for different estimates of the line of best fit. The most accurate approach to linear regression is to use a graphing calculator, which calculates the one most mathematically precise line of best fit.

Example 3

A concert hall owner kept track of how the number of people at the hall was related to the cost of tickets for each band. The table shows the data he collected.

Cost per Ticket (in dollars), c	Number of People, n
20	175
35	131
15	241
40	107
30	123
10	265
45	88

What equation represents the line of best fit for the data set, with slope and y-intercept rounded to the nearest integers? Predict the number of people at the concert hall for a concert where tickets cost $25.

Strategy   **Use a graphing calculator.**

Step 1   Enter the data in the graphing calculator.

Press STAT , and then select 1: Edit.

Enter the cost per ticket under L_1 and the number of people under L_2 for each data pair in the table.

L_1	L_2	L_3
20	175	----
35	131	
15	241	
40	107	
30	123	
10	265	
45	88	

Step 2   Create a scatterplot of the data.

Press 2nd Y= to access the STAT PLOT function and choose Plot1. Make sure the plot is ON and the scatterplot icon is highlighted.

The independent (x) values are the ticket prices (c), and the dependent (y) values are the number of people (n). So enter L_1 (the list of c-values) for XList and L_2 (the list of n-values) for YList.

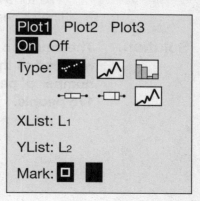

Plot1   Plot2   Plot3
On   Off
Type:
XList: L1
YList: L2
Mark: □ ■

Press ZOOM, and choose number 9: ZoomStat to see the scatterplot. Adjust the windows as needed.

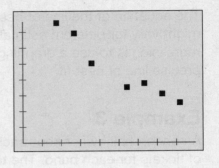

Step 3 Have the calculator determine the line of best fit.

Press STAT, scroll to the right for the CALC menu, and choose number 4: LinReg(ax + b).

List the parameters "L_1, L_2, Y_1." (Use VARS and choose Y-VARS and Function to get Y_1.)

Press ENTER. The values shown for a and b complete the equation of the line of best fit in the form $y = ax + b$. The screen shows a equal to -4.984931507, which rounds to -5. The screen shows b equal to 300.2945205, which rounds to 300.

The line of best fit is approximately $y = -5x + 300$, or $n = -5c + 300$.

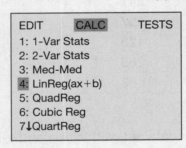
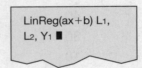
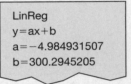

Step 4 Predict the number of people, n, when $c = 25$.

Hit GRAPH to graph the line of best fit.

Press TRACE, and then ▲. Type 25 and press ENTER.

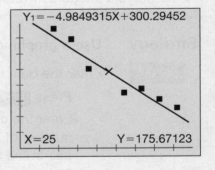

A number of people must be a whole number, so round the y-value of 175.67123 up to 176.

Note that the rounded values in the equation $n = -5c + 300$ would produce an n-value of 175 for a c-value of 25. However, the graphing calculator, by using the actual line of best fit, produced a more accurate n-value prediction of 176.

Solution **The equation representing the line of best fit with slope and y-intercept rounded to the nearest integers is $n = -5c + 300$. The best prediction of the number of people in the concert hall for a concert where tickets cost \$25 is 176 people.**

Coached Example

Wiley Appliances kept track of the average cost per appliance repair based on the age of the appliance. The data are displayed in the scatterplot to the right.

Draw a line of best fit for the data. Then find the equation of the line and use it to predict the cost of repairing a 5-year-old appliance.

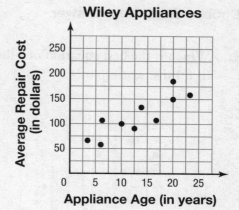

Wiley Appliances

Draw a line of best fit for the data.

Using two points on your line, find the slope.

Two points on the line are (_____, _____) and (_____, _____).

$m = \dfrac{y_2 - y_1}{x_2 - x_1} =$ _____ = _____ = _____

The slope is _____.

A point on the line is (_____, _____).

Use the point-slope form of a line to find the equation of the line of best fit.

$$y - y_1 = m(x - x_1)$$

$y -$ _____ = _____ $(x -$ _____)

Write your equation in slope-intercept form by simplifying and solving for y.

_____

_____

The equation is _____.

The x-values represent _____.

The y-values represent _____.

Substitute 5 for x in your line-of-best-fit equation. _____

Simplify. y = _____

The equation of the line of best fit is _____.

The average cost of repair for a 5-year-old appliance is about _____.

Choose the correct answer.

1. Which is the best equation of a line of best fit for this scatterplot?

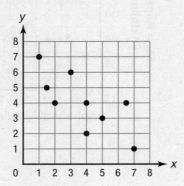

A. $y = x + 8$

B. $y = {}^-x + 8$

C. $y = 8x$

D. $y = {}^-8x$

2. Which is the best equation of a line of best fit for this scatterplot?

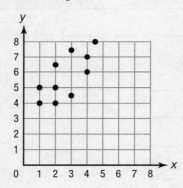

A. $y = 3x$

B. $y = x + 3$

C. $y = {}^-x + 3$

D. $y = \frac{1}{3}x + 3$

Use the information and scatterplot below for questions 3 and 4.

The owner of a water park recorded the average daily temperature and the number of tickets sold for each day in June. The data is displayed on the scatterplot below.

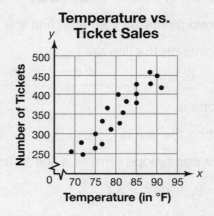

3. Which is the best equation of a line of best fit for this scatterplot?

A. $y = {}^-10x + 1{,}050$

B. $y = \frac{1}{10}x + 441$

C. $y = 15x - 825$

D. $y = 10x - 450$

4. Based on the equation of the line of best fit, which is the best production of the number of tickets that will be sold on a day when the average temperature reaches 100°F?

A. 500

B. 525

C. 550

D. 575

5. Which is the best equation of a line of best fit for this scatterplot?

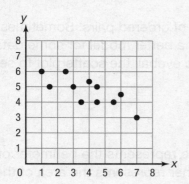

A. $y = -\frac{1}{2}x + 6\frac{1}{2}$

B. $y = -6x$

C. $y = -x + 6$

D. $y = \frac{1}{2}x + 6\frac{1}{2}$

6. The scatterplot below shows the heights, in inches, and weights, in pounds, of 14 basketball players.

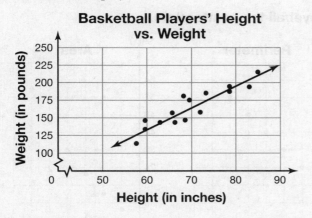

According to the line of best fit, what is the best estimate of the weight of a basketball player who is 75 inches tall?

A. 197 pounds   C. 157 pounds

B. 177 pounds   D. 137 pounds

7. Which is the best equation of a line of best fit for this scatterplot?

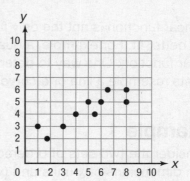

A. $y = -\frac{1}{2}x + 2$ C. $y = 2x + 1$

B. $y = -2x + 1$ D. $y = \frac{1}{2}x + 2$

8. Students in a biology class measured the length of a vine on different days of the month to determine its rate of growth. The table below shows the length of the vine on different days.

Day	Length (in centimeters)
1	20
3	21
5	22
8	23
9	24
13	25
15	26
16	27
17	28

Which equation is closest to the line of best fit for this data?

A. $y = -0.5x + 20$

B. $y = -0.5x - 20$

C. $y = 0.5x + 20$

D. $y = 0.5x - 20$

Curve of Best Fit

SOL: A.11

A linear function is not the only function model for a set of ordered pairs. Sometimes a curve is a better fit. For example, a quadratic function may be a better model for some data than a linear function. One way to determine which is best is to eyeball the scatterplot to see if the data points resemble a line or a curve.

Example 1

Consider the two sets of ordered pairs below. One table represents the perimeter of a rectangle with dimensions of x units and $(x + 4)$ units, and the other represents the area of the same rectangle. Which should be modeled by a linear function? Which should be modeled by a quadratic function?

Perimeter			Area	
x	$P(x)$		x	$A(x)$
1	12		1	5
2	16		2	12
3	20		3	21
4	24		4	32
5	28		5	45
6	32		6	60

Strategy **Graph each set of points, and eyeball the scatterplots.**

The points on the perimeter scatterplot lie exactly in a straight line. So a linear function perfectly fits this graph.

The points on the area scatterplot lie along a curve that appears to be part of a parabola. So a quadratic function fits this graph.

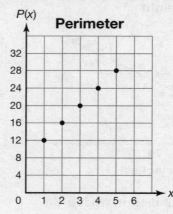

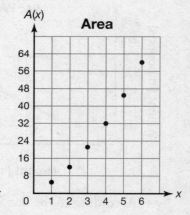

Solution **A linear function is the best model for the first table of values. A quadratic function is the best model for the second table of values.**

In Example 1, the data showing the area of the rectangle could be modeled perfectly by the quadratic function $y = x^2 + 4x$. In real life, usually no one algebraic model fits perfectly. **Curve fitting** means finding the curve that fits best.

In Example 2, you will use a graphing calculator to perform a **quadratic regression.** This is a statistical method that fits a quadratic function to a set of data.

Example 2

Use quadratic regression to find the equation for the curve that best fits the table showing the area of the rectangle from Example 1.

Area

x	A(x)
1	5
2	12
3	21
4	32
5	45
6	60

Strategy   **Use your graphing calculator.**

Step 1   Graph the points on your graphing calculator.

Enter the data into lists L_1 and L_2 on your calculator.

Display the scatterplot.

Adjust the windows on your calculator as needed to view the scatterplot.

Step 2   Use your calculator to perform quadratic regression.

Press STAT . Scroll to the right to select the CALC menu, and then select number 5: QuadReg.

QuadReg
$y=ax^2+bx+c$
$a=1$
$b=4$
$c=0$
■

Press VARS ▶ Y-VARS.

Press 1 to select 1: Function and then 1 to select 1: Y_1.

This instructs the calculator to input the equation for you as Y_1.

Now press ENTER twice.

A quadratic model is of the form $y = ax^2 + bx + c$. So this model is $A(x) = x^2 + 4x + 0$, or $y = x^2 + 4x$.

Step 3   Display the scatterplot and function model to check that your answer is reasonable.

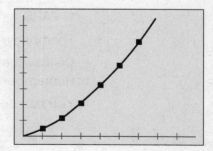

If you press Y= , you will see that the equation for the line is already input for Y_1. Actually, your calculator probably shows something that looks more complicated, such as $y_1 = .99999999999969x^2 + 4.0000000000022x + 0$. If you round these values, the equation is equal to $y = x^2 + 4x + 0$, or $y = x^2 + 4x$.

Solution   **The equation of the quadratic model is $A(x) = x^2 + 4x$.**

You can use a best-fitting quadratic model to make predictions.

Example 3

A company began producing an environmentally safe household cleaner in 2004. The table to the right shows the number of units of the product sold over the first 7 years it was on the market.

Find the best-fitting quadratic model for the sales of the product. Explain why a quadratic model is a better fit than a linear model. Predict how many units the company will sell in 2013.

Year	Units Sold (in ten thousands)
2004 (0)	1
2005 (1)	1
2006 (2)	3
2007 (3)	6
2008 (4)	11
2009 (5)	18
2010 (6)	26

Strategy **Use your graphing calculator.**

Step 1 Enter the data into lists L_1 and L_2 on your calculator.

Let 0 represent year 2004, let 1 represent year 2005, and so on.

Step 2 Use your calculator to perform quadratic regression.

Follow the same steps you used in Example 2. The equation for the model is
$y = 0.82x^2 - 0.75x + 1$.

```
QuadReg
  y=ax²+bx+c
  a=.8214285714
  b=−.75
  c=1
  R²=.9997382199
■
```

Step 3 Show that this quadratic model is better than a linear model.

Be sure that the equation for the quadratic model is entered as Y_1 on your calculator.

Then use linear regression to find the best-fitting regression line for the model. Enter the equation for that linear function as Y_2 on your calculator.

To do this, after you press 4: LinReg(ax + b) on your calculator, press VARS Y-VARS.

Then press 1 to select 1: Function and then 2 to select 2: Y_2.

Display the scatterplot and both function models on your calculator. Remember to use STAT PLOT to set Plot2 to ON.

You can see that the quadratic model is a better fit.

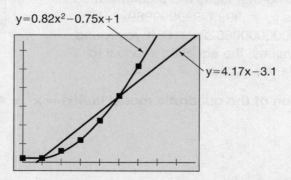

$y=0.82x^2-0.75x+1$

$y=4.17x-3.1$

Step 4   Use the model to predict the sales in 2013.

If 6 represents year 2010, then 9 represents year 2013. Substitute that value for x and solve for y.

$y = 0.82x^2 - 0.75x + 1 = (0.82)(9^2) - (0.75)(9) + 1 \approx 60.7$

This means that 60.7 ten thousands, or about 607,000 units, will be sold.

Solution   **The equation of the quadratic model is $y = 0.82x^2 - 0.75x + 1$. A quadratic model fits the points better than does a linear model. The company will sell about 607,000 units in 2013.**

Example 4

The manager of a large bookstore counts the number of books that are sold each hour since the store has opened. For example, since the store opens at 8:00 A.M., she will record the number of books sold from 8:00 A.M. to 9:00 A.M. as the number sold in the first hour. The table below shows some of her data.

Book Store Sales

Hours Since Opening	0	4	8	12	16
Number of Books	0	26	38	37	22

Write an equation for a function to model the data. Then use that function to predict the maximum number of books sold in an hour that day.

Strategy   **Use your graphing calculator.**

Step 1   Enter the data into lists L_1 and L_2 on your calculator.

Step 2   Use your calculator to perform quadratic regression.

The equation for the model is
$y = -0.42x^2 + 8.16x + 0.03$.

```
QuadReg
 y=ax²+bx+c
 a=-.4241071429
 b=8.160714286
 c=.0285714286
 R²=.9999396718

■
```

Step 3
Graph the model, and find its maximum.

Graph the scatterplot. Adjust the window as needed.

Press 2nd TRACE to access the CALC menu. Press 4 to select 4: maximum.

The screen asks "Left Bound?" Use the arrow keys to move the cursor to the left of the maximum point. Press ENTER.

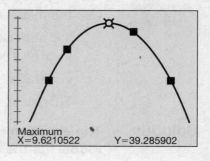

The screen asks "Right Bound?" Use the arrow keys to move the cursor to the right of the maximum point. Press ENTER.

Then press ENTER again.

Remember, the maximum is the greatest y-value.

The calculator shows that the maximum is 39.3 when $x \approx 9.62$.

Since a store cannot sell 0.3 of a book, predict 39 as the maximum.

Solution The equation of the quadratic model is $y = {}^{-}0.42x^2 + 8.16x + 0.03$. A good prediction of the maximum number of books sold in any one hour is 39.

Coached Example

A projectile is shot upward from a point that is 5 feet above the ground. The table below shows the height of the projectile at various times.

Time (in seconds)	Height (in feet)
0	5
2	157
3	185
5	145
6	77

Write an equation for a quadratic function that models this situation.

Use your graphing calculator. Enter the data in lists L_1 and L_2 of your calculator.

Use your calculator to perform quadratic regression. Follow the same steps you used in Example 2.

The calculator shows that $a =$ _____, $b =$ _____, and $c =$ _____.

The equation for the quadratic model is $y =$ _____$x^2 +$ _____$x +$ _____.

The equation for the curve of best fit is _____.

Lesson Practice

Choose the correct answer.

Use this table for questions 1 and 2.

The average quarterly stock prices of a new company for its first two years of business are shown in the table below.

Quarter	Price Per Share (in $)
1	2.00
2	8.00
3	12.50
4	15.50
5	17.00
6	17.00
7	16.00
8	13.00

1. Which equation shows the quadratic model that best fits these data?

   A. $y = 1.6x^2 + 5.6x$

   B. $y = 1.6x^2 - 5.6x$

   C. $y = -0.7x^2 + 8.1x + 5.3$

   D. $y = -0.7x^2 + 8.1x - 5.3$

2. If the trend continues, which is the best prediction of the price per share in Quarter 10?

   A. $1.00

   B. $3.00

   C. $9.00

   D. $10.00

3. An object was thrown from the top of a building. The table below shows the height of the object at various times.

Time (in seconds)	Height (in feet)
1	148
2	156
3	145
4	118
5	76

Using a best-fitting quadratic model, which is the best prediction of the time when the ball will be about 2 feet above the ground?

   A. 5.7 seconds

   B. 5.9 seconds

   C. 6.2 seconds

   D. 6.7 seconds

4. Which of the following sets of data can best be represented by a quadratic curve of best fit?

   A.
x	0	1	2	3	4
y	15	12	9	6	3

   B.
x	6	8	10	12	14
y	1	7	14	19	25

   C.
x	3	4	5	6	7
y	6	14	24	36	50

   D.
x	2	4	6	8	10
y	17	9	2	-6	-15

Use these data for questions 5 and 6.

The table below shows how the annual costs of attending a college have changed from school year to school year.

Year (x)	Annual Cost in Dollars (y)
2002–2003 (0)	17,200
2003–2004 (1)	17,750
2004–2005 (2)	18,500
2005–2006 (3)	20,000
2006–2007 (4)	21,500
2007–2008 (5)	23,500
2008–2009 (6)	26,000

5. Which model best fits these data, where x represents the number of years since 2002–2003?

   A. $y = 190x^2 + 318x + 17{,}206$

   B. $y = 190x^2 - 318x + 17{,}206$

   C. $y = 1{,}460x + 16{,}253$

   D. $y = 1{,}460x^2 + 16{,}253x$

6. If the trend shown in the table continued, which school year would you expect to have been the first to have an annual cost greater than $30,000?

   A. 2009–2010

   B. 2010–2011

   C. 2011–2012

   D. 2012–2013

Use these data for questions 7 and 8.

The braking distance for a car is a function of the speed at which it was traveling. The table below shows the speed, in miles per hour, and total stopping distance, in feet, for a particular car.

Speed (in mph)	Braking Distance (in ft)
10	17
20	43
30	82
40	132
50	194
60	265

7. Which quadratic model best fits these data?

   A. $y = 4.98x^2 - 52.1x$

   B. $y = 4.98x^2 + 52.1x$

   C. $y = 0.06x^2 - 1.02x + 0.7$

   D. $y = 0.06x^2 + 1.02x + 0.7$

8. Which is the best prediction of what the total stopping distance will be if the car is traveling 65 miles per hour?

   A. 271 feet

   B. 306 feet

   C. 349 feet

   D. 377 feet

Chapter 4 Review

1. Larissa sells hats at a clothing store. She noticed that there is a correlation between the number of hats sold and the outside temperature. The graph below models the relationship between the daily high temperature and the number of hats Larissa sold over a 10-day period.

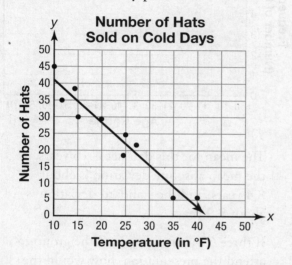

According to the line of best fit, how many hats can Larissa expect to sell on a day with an outside temperature of 30°F?

   A.   5

   B.   10

   C.   15

   D.   20

2. This line plot shows the mass, in kilograms, of 10 packages waiting to be shipped.

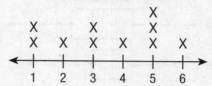

The mean mass of the packages is 3.5 kg. What is the mean absolute deviation of the mass of the packages?

   A.   0.5 kg

   B.   1 kg

   C.   1.5 kg

   D.   5 kg

Use the information and box-and-whisker plot for questions 3 and 4.

This double box-and-whisker plot compares the heights of 20 basketball players in two different intramural leagues.

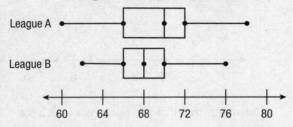

Height of Players (in inches)

3. Which statement below is **not** true?

   A. The lower quartile values for both samples are the same.

   B. The median height for the League A sample is greater than the median height for the League B sample.

   C. The sample for League A has a greater interquartile range than the sample for League B.

   D. The upper quartile values for both samples are the same.

4. Which league has the greater range in the players' heights and by how much?

   A. The sample for League A has the greater range in players' heights, by 2 inches.

   B. The sample for League A has the greater range in players' heights, by 4 inches.

   C. The sample for League A has the greater range in players' heights, by 6 inches.

   D. The sample for League A has the greater range in players' heights, by 8 inches.

5. Jana recorded the ages of all the people attending a historical museum's presentation today. The histogram below represents this information.

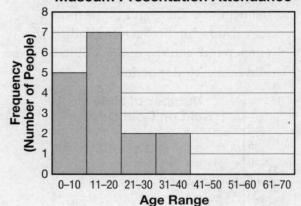

The mean for this data set is 16 years, the mean absolute deviation is about 8.4 years, and the standard deviation is about 9.9 years.

If three 65-year-olds joined the group to attend the presentation, how would the mean absolute deviation and standard deviation be affected?

   A. They would both decrease and also become closer together in value.

   B. They would both decrease and also become further apart in value.

   C. They would both increase and also become closer together in value.

   D. They would both increase and also become further apart in value.

6. Distances traveled and airfares are often related. The table and scatterplot below show several randomly selected trips (rounded to the nearest 50 miles) and their round-trip airfares.

Distance Traveled (in miles), d	Airfare (in dollars), a
1,500	239
800	199
500	179
2,300	300
950	220
250	189
650	140
1,800	259

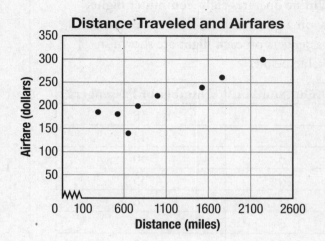

Which equation most closely represents a line of best fit for the data?

A. $a = 0.06d + 145$

B. $a = 0.6d + 100$

C. $a = {}^-0.6d + 310$

D. $a = {}^-0.06d + 350$

7. A farmer is trying to determine how much fertilizer to use on his crop fields. He tried using different amounts of fertilizer, measured in pounds per acre. Then he recorded the yields for those fields, in bushels per acre (bu/acre). This table shows his data.

Fertilizer Used (in lb/acre), x	50	70	90	110	130	150	170
Yield (in bu/acre), y	40	61	75	83	85	80	69

Which equation most closely represents a curve of best fit for the data?

A. $y = {}^-0.008x^2 - 2x + 40$

B. $y = {}^-0.008x^2 + 2x - 40$

C. $y = 0.008x^2 - 2x + 40$

D. $y = 0.008x^2 + 2x + 40$

Use the information below for questions 8–10.

An airline operates eight commuter flights daily on a given route. The average numbers of passengers on each flight are shown in the table below.

Flight Number	Number of Passengers
1	38
2	43
3	40
4	35
5	26
6	25
7	35
8	38

The mean number of passengers per flight on this route is 35.

8. What is the standard deviation for these data?

   A. 2.25 passengers

   B. 4.75 passengers

   C. 6 passengers

   D. 8 passengers

9. How many of the daily flights have an average number of passengers that lies within one standard deviation of the mean?

   A. 2   C. 4

   B. 3   D. 5

10. Which flight has an average number of passengers that represents a z-score of $^-1.5$?

    A. Flight #2   C. Flight #6

    B. Flight #5   D. Flight #8

11. The mean price of a bike in Paul's used bike store is $75, with a standard deviation of $12. If Lucas buys a bike there for $60, what z-score represents the price of this bike?

    A. $^-1.25$

    B. $^-0.\overline{6}$

    C. $0.\overline{6}$

    D. 1.25

12. An electric company compared the mean daily temperature in degrees Fahrenheit with the mean daily consumption in kilowatt-hours per household. The results are shown in the table below.

Mean Daily Temperature (in °F), t	Mean Daily Consumption (in kWh), c
31	56
34	50
39	48
40	45
46	42
51	40
53	40
60	35

Which equation most closely represents a line of best fit for the data?

A. $c = 2t - 8$

B. $c = -\frac{2}{3}t + 74$

C. $c = -\frac{3}{2}t + 125$

D. $c = -2t + 119$

13. This semester, Charlaine took 10 quizzes in her math class and 10 quizzes in her English class. The table below shows each set of quiz scores she earned, arranged from lowest to highest.

Math Quiz Scores	82	85	85	90	91	91	91	94	95	96
English Quiz Scores	72	74	74	79	87	87	89	92	92	94

A. Calculate the mean, mean absolute deviation, variance, and standard deviation of quiz scores for each class. Show your work.

B. For which set of quiz scores is there greater dispersion from the mean?

_____

C. The box-and-whisker plots below summarize the quiz score data. Compare the interquartile ranges of the two data sets.

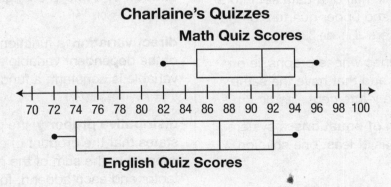

Charlaine's Quizzes

Math Quiz Scores

English Quiz Scores

Glossary

abscissa the x-value of the ordered pair (x, y) (Lesson 25)

addition property of equality the property that states if $a = b$, then $a + c = b + c$ and $c + a = c + b$ (Lesson 9)

additive axiom of inequality the axiom that states if $a > b$, then $a + c > b + c$ (Lesson 18)

algebraic expression a combination of numbers and variables that includes one or more operations (Lesson 1)

area the amount of space covered by a two-dimensional figure, measured in square units (Lesson 4)

arithmetic sequence a sequence in which a common number is added to each term to get to the next term (Lesson 24)

base in an exponential expression, the number that is used as a factor the number of times indicated by the exponent (Lesson 2)

binomial a polynomial with two terms (Lesson 3)

box-and-whisker plot a data display that separates the middle half of a data set into a box and the lower and upper quarters of the data set into whiskers (Lesson 33)

coincident lines lines whose graphs lie on top of one another and that have the same slope and the same y-intercept (Lesson 15)

consistent system of equations a system of equations that has at least one solution (Lesson 15)

constant of proportionality see constant of variation (Lessons 27 and 28)

constant of variation the value of k in $y = kx$, the equation of a direct variation, or in $y = \frac{k}{x}$, the equation of an inverse variation (Lessons 27 and 28)

cube a number to multiply a number by itself twice or to raise it to the power of 3 (Lesson 1)

cube root one of the three equal factors of a number (Lesson 1)

curve fitting the act of finding the curve that best fits a set of ordered pairs plotted on the coordinate plane (Lesson 35)

dependent system of equations a consistent system of equations where one linear equation is a multiple of the other and, therefore, has an infinite number of solutions (Lesson 15)

dependent variable a variable that represents the elements of the range, or set of outputs, for a relation or function (Lesson 25)

difference of two squares a binomial where one perfect square is subtracted from another perfect square (Lesson 5)

dilation of a line a change to the slope of a line (Lesson 14)

direct variation a function in which the ratio of the dependent variable to the independent variable is constant; a function in the form $y = kx$ (Lesson 27)

distributive property the property that states that the product of a factor and a sum is equal to the sum of the products of the factor and each addend; for example, $a(b + c) = ab + ac$ (Lesson 4)

division property of equality the property that states if $a = b$ and $c \neq 0$, then $a \div c = b \div c$ (Lesson 9)

domain the set of all the first coordinates, or x-values, in the ordered pairs that represent a relation (Lesson 25)

exponent a superscript number that indicates how many times to use another number, called a base, as a factor (Lesson 2)

extremes the least and greatest values in a data set (Lesson 33)

factoring (a polynomial) writing a polynomial as the product of two or more factors (Lesson 5)

first quartile see lower quartile (Lessons 31 and 33)

FOIL a method of multiplying two binomials by finding the sum of the products of the First terms, Outer terms, Inner terms, and Last terms; $(a + b)(c + d) = ac + ad + bc + bd$ (Lesson 4)

formula a literal equation that represents a general relationship among quantities (Lesson 10)

function a relation in which each input number, or x-value, has one and only one output number, or y-value (Lessons 11 and 23)

function notation an expression such as $f(x)$ used to name a function and represent the range values for the domain values represented by x (Lesson 24)

greatest common factor (GCF) the greatest number or expression that is a factor of two or more numbers or expressions (Lesson 5)

half plane the portion of the coordinate plane lying on one side of a line (Lesson 19)

inconsistent system of equations a system of equations that has no solution (Lesson 15)

independent system of equations a consistent system of equations with only one solution (Lesson 15)

independent variable a variable that represents the elements of the domain, or set of inputs, for a relation or function (Lesson 25)

indirect variation see inverse variation (Lesson 28)

inductive reasoning the process of observing patterns and using the patterns to make generalizations (Lesson 2)

inequality a mathematical sentence showing the relationship between quantities that are not equal, using $<$, $>$, $\leq$, $\geq$, or $\neq$ (Lesson 18)

interquartile range the difference between the upper and lower quartiles in a data set (Lessons 31 and 33)

inverse variation a function in which the product of the dependent variable and the independent variable is constant; a function in the form $y = \frac{k}{x}$ (Lesson 28)

like terms terms that contain the same variable(s) raised to the same power(s) (Lesson 3)

line of best fit the line that most closely represents the relationship between the two variables for data in a scatterplot (Lesson 34)

linear equation an equation in which the variable or variables are raised to the first power and that forms a straight line when graphed (Lessons 9 and 13)

linear inequality an inequality in which the variable or variables are raised to the first power (Lesson 18)

linear regression the process of finding the line of best fit for a set of data (Lesson 34)

literal equation an equation that contains more than one variable (Lesson 10)

lower quartile the median of the lower half of the numbers in a data set (Lessons 31 and 33)

mean (arithmetic mean) the quantity found by adding the values in a set and dividing by the number of values (Lesson 29)

mean absolute deviation (MAD) the arithmetic mean of the absolute values of the deviations of each data point from the mean of the data set (Lesson 29)

median the middle term, or the average of the two middle terms, when the terms in a data set are arranged from least to greatest (Lessons 31 and 33)

monomial a polynomial with one term (Lesson 3)

multiplication property of equality the property that states if $a = b$, then $ac = bc$ and $ca = cb$ (Lesson 9)

negative multiplication axiom of inequality the axiom that states if $c < 0$, then $a > b$ if and only if $ac < bc$ (Lesson 18)

negative powers and reciprocals changing the sign of an exponent by moving the expression from the numerator to the denominator or from the denominator to the numerator; for example, $a^{-n} = \frac{1}{a^n}$, if $a \neq 0$ and $\frac{1}{a^{-n}} = \frac{a^n}{1} = a^n$, if $a \neq 0$ (Lesson 2)

order of operations the rules for evaluating an expression: parentheses first, then exponents, next multiplication and division (from left to right), and finally addition and subtraction (from left to right) (Lesson 8)

ordinate the y-value of the ordered pair (x, y) (Lesson 25)

outlier an element in a data set that falls at least 1.5 times the interquartile range below the lower quartile or above the upper quartile (Lesson 31)

parallel lines lines with the same slope but different y-intercepts; lines that never intersect (Lesson 12)

perfect cube a number whose cube root is an integer (Lesson 1)

perfect square a number whose square root is an integer, or a variable raised to an even power (Lesson 1)

perimeter the distance around a figure, or the sum of the lengths of the sides of a polygon (Lesson 3)

perpendicular lines lines that intersect at right angles (Lesson 12)

point-slope form of a linear equation a linear equation expressed in the form $y - y_1 = m(x - x_1)$, where m is the slope and (x_1, y_1) are the coordinates of a point on the line (Lesson 13)

polynomial a term or expression that contains one or more variables or constants (Lesson 3)

positive multiplication axiom of inequality the axiom that states if $c > 0$, then $a > b$ if and only if $ac > bc$ (Lesson 18)

power of a power the rule stating that when a number in exponential form is raised to a power, the exponents are multiplied; for example, $(a^m)^n = a^{mn}$ (Lesson 2)

power of a product the rule stating that when a product is raised to a power, the powers of each factor are multiplied; for example, $(ab)^m = a^m b^m$ (Lesson 2)

power of a quotient the rule stating that when a quotient is raised to a power, both the numerator and the denominator are raised to that power; for example, $\left(\frac{a}{b}\right)^m = \frac{a^m}{b^m}$, if $b \neq 0$ (Lesson 2)

power of zero the rule stating that any nonzero number raised to the power of zero is 1; for example, $a^0 = 1$, if $a \neq 0$ (Lesson 2)

prime polynomial a polynomial that is not factorable (Lesson 5)

principal square root the positive square root of a number (Lesson 1)

product of powers the rule stating that when multiplying powers with the same base, the exponents are added; for example, $a^m \cdot a^n = a^{m+n}$ (Lesson 2)

product property of square roots the rule that states that the square root of a product is equal to the product of the square roots of the factors; for example, $\sqrt{ab} = \sqrt{a} \cdot \sqrt{b}$ (Lesson 1)

quadratic equation an equation in which the greatest power of any variable is 2 (Lesson 21)

quadratic regression a statistical method used to fit a quadratic function to a set of data (Lesson 35)

quotient of powers the rule stating that when finding the quotient of powers with the same base, the exponents are subtracted; for example, $\frac{a^m}{a^n} = a^{m-n}$, if $a \neq 0$ (Lesson 2)

quotient property of square roots the rule that states that the square root of a quotient is equal to the quotient of the square root of the dividend and the square root of the divisor; for example, $\sqrt{\frac{a}{b}} = \frac{\sqrt{a}}{\sqrt{b}}$ (Lesson 1)

radicand a number or expression under a radical symbol (Lesson 1)

range (of a relation) the set of all the second coordinates, or y-values, in the ordered pairs that represent a relation (Lesson 25)

range (of a set of data) the difference between the least and greatest values in a data set (Lesson 33)

relation a set of ordered pairs that connects a set of output numbers, or y-values, to a set of input numbers, or x-values (Lesson 23)

root for a given function $f(x)$, a value of x that makes $f(x)$ equal to zero; also called a zero of the function (Lesson 22)

scientific notation a number written as the product of a power of 10 and a decimal number greater than or equal to 1 and less than 10 (Lesson 2)

slope the ratio of the change in vertical distance to the corresponding change in horizontal distance between two points on a line; slope is a measure of the steepness of the line (Lesson 12)

slope-intercept form of a linear equation a linear equation expressed in the form $y = mx + b$, where m is the slope and b is the y-intercept (Lesson 13)

square a number to multiply a number by itself or to raise it to the power of 2 (Lesson 1)

square root one of the two equal factors of a number (Lesson 1)

standard deviation a measure of dispersion for a data set, equal to the square root of the variance; the symbol σ stands for the population standard deviation, and S stands for the sample standard deviation (Lesson 30)

standard form of a linear equation a linear equation of the form $Ax + By = C$, where A, B and C are real numbers and A and B are both not zero (Lesson 13)

substitution property of equality the property that states if $a = b$, then a can be substituted for b in any equation or inequality (Lesson 9)

subtraction property of equality the property that states if $a = b$, then $a - c = b - c$ (Lesson 9)

symmetric property of equality the property that states if $a = b$, then $b = a$ (Lesson 9)

system of linear equations a set of two or more linear equations in the same variables (Lesson 15)

system of linear inequalities a set of two or more linear inequalities in the same variables (Lesson 20)

term a number, a variable, or the product of a number and one or more variables (Lesson 3)

third quartile see upper quartile (Lessons 31 and 33)

transitive axiom of inequality the axiom that states if $a > b$ and $b > c$, then $a > c$ (Lesson 18)

transitive property of equality the property that states if $a = b$ and $b = c$, then $a = c$ (Lesson 9)

translation of a line a vertical shift of a line, without changing its slope (Lesson 14)

trinomial a polynomial with three terms (Lesson 3)

upper quartile the median of the upper half of the numbers in a data set (Lessons 31 and 33)

variable a symbol or letter, such as x, that is used to represent a number (Lesson 1)

variance the arithmetic mean of the squared deviations from the mean of a data set; the symbol σ^2 represents the variance of a population and the symbol S^2 represents the variance of a sample (Lesson 30)

vertical line test a method to test whether or not a graphed relation is a function; if any vertical line intersects the graph of a relation more than once, the relation is not a function (Lesson 23)

x-intercept(s) the point(s) where a graph intersects the x-axis (Lesson 12)

y-intercept(s) the point(s) where a graph intersects the y-axis (Lesson 12)

zero product property the property that states the product of two numbers is zero if and only if one or both of the numbers is zero; if $ab = 0$, then $a = 0$ and/or $b = 0$ (Lesson 22)

zero(s) of a function for a function $\{x, f(x)\}$, the value or values of x that make $f(x) = 0$; the x-coordinate(s) of the point(s) where the graph of a function crosses the x-axis (Lesson 21)

z-score a measurement that indicates the number of standard deviations a data value lies above or below the mean of the data set (Lesson 32)

**Virginia End-of-Course Coach
Algebra I**

Practice Test 1

Name: _____

Directions

Read each question and choose the best answer. For this test you may assume that the value of the denominator is not zero.

SAMPLE

Which expression is equivalent to $(x - 2)(3x^2 + x - 8)$?

A $3x^3 - 5x^2 - 6x + 16$

B $3x^3 - 5x^2 - 6x - 16$

C $3x^3 - 5x^2 - 10x + 16$

D $3x^3 - 5x^2 - 10x - 16$

GO ON

1 Which polynomial is equivalent to the following expression?

$$(6x^2 - 4x + 7) + (2x - 9)$$

A $6x^2 - 6x - 2$
B $6x^2 - 2x - 2$
C $6x^2 + 6x + 16$
D $8x^2 - 4x - 2$

2 What is the value of the expression $xy^2 + 6y$, if $x = {}^-2$ and $y = 5$?

F $^-70$
G $^-20$
H 80
J 130

3 Which of the following is equivalent to $\left(\dfrac{x^3}{y}\right)^5$?

A $\dfrac{x^{15}}{y^5}$
B $\dfrac{x^{15}}{y^6}$
C $\dfrac{x^8}{y^5}$
D $\dfrac{x^8}{y^6}$

4 Which of the following equals $3x^2 + 9x - 30$ when factored completely?

F $3(x^2 + 3x + 10)$
G $3(x + 10)(x - 1)$
H $3(x + 6)(x - 5)$
J $3(x + 5)(x - 2)$

5 What is $\sqrt{450}$ expressed in *simplest* radical form?

A $15\sqrt{2}$
B $30\sqrt{5}$
C $5\sqrt{18}$
D $3\sqrt{50}$

6 The amount of time Chris spent on his science fair project was 3 hours less than twice the amount of time Ying-Ying spent on her science fair project. If Ying-Ying spent 5 hours on her science fair project, how many hours did Chris spend on his?

F 2
G 4
H 6
J 7

7 Which expression is equivalent to $(x^2 - 9x + 20) \div (x - 4)$?

A $x + 10$
B $x + 5$
C $x - 5$
D $x - 10$

GO ON

8 Which labeled point on the number line is closest to the square root of 77?

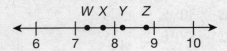

F W

G X

H Y

J Z

9 Which is equivalent to the following expression?

$$(-3x^2y)^4$$

A $-12x^6y^4$

B $-12x^8y^4$

C $81x^6y^4$

D $81x^8y^4$

10 $\square = X^2$ $\square = X$ $\square = 1$

Based on the models for x^2, x, and 1, which product is represented by the diagram?

F $(x + 4)(x + 1)$

G $(x + 4)(2x + 1)$

H $(x + 4)(2x^2 + 1)$

J $(x^2 + 4x)(2x^2 + x)$

11 What is the value of the expression $\sqrt[3]{9x + 2y^2}$ when $x = 3$ and $y = 7$?

A 3

B 5

C 17

D 101

12 What is $\sqrt[3]{128}$ expressed in *simplest* radical form?

F $4\sqrt[3]{2}$

G $8\sqrt[3]{2}$

H $4\sqrt[3]{4}$

J $2\sqrt[3]{16}$

13 A factored form of $x^2 + 5x - 36$ is –

A $(x - 12)(x + 3)$

B $(x - 6)(x + 6)$

C $(x - 4)(x + 9)$

D $(x - 3)(x + 12)$

14 Which of the following is equivalent to $\dfrac{x^4y^2}{x^2y^4}$?

F $\dfrac{x^2}{y^2}$

G $\dfrac{y^2}{x^2}$

H x^2y^2

J x^6y^6

GO ON

15 What is the slope of a line that passes through the points $(-2, 0)$ and $(4, 4)$?

A $-\frac{2}{3}$ C $\frac{1}{2}$

B $-\frac{1}{2}$ D $\frac{2}{3}$

16 What is the solution to the inequality below?

$$3x - 6 < 18$$

F $x < 4$ H $x < 8$

G $x > 4$ J $x > 8$

17 If $2s = r$ and $r = s - 3$, what property of equality justifies writing the equation $2s = s - 3$?

A Addition property

B Multiplication property

C Transitive property

D Symmetric property

18 The formula for finding the volume of a cylinder is $V = \pi r^2 h$, where r represents the radius and h represents the height. Which equation can you use to find the height, h, of the cylinder?

F $h = V - \pi r^2$

G $h = \dfrac{V}{\pi r^2}$

H $h = \dfrac{\pi V}{r^2}$

J $h = \dfrac{V r^2}{\pi}$

19 What is the solution of the system of equations shown?

$$\begin{cases} x + 8 = y \\ 2y + 5x = -5 \end{cases}$$

A $(-3, 5)$ C $(2, -10)$

B $(-2, 6)$ D $(13, 5)$

20 The function $y = x^2 + 6x + 11$ is graphed below.

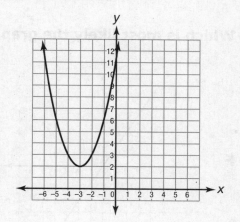

Which of the following is the solution set to the equation $x^2 + 6x + 11 = 0$?

F $-3, 2$

G $0, 11$

H 11

J There are no real solutions.

21 Which is an equation of a line with a slope of 5 that passes through the origin?

A $x = 5$ C $x = 5y$

B $y = 5$ D $y = 5x$

GO ON

22 The equation $y = \frac{1}{2}x$ is shown on the graph below.

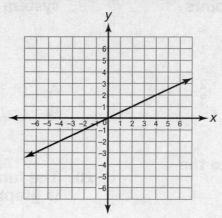

Which is most likely the graph of $y = \frac{1}{2}x - 2$?

F

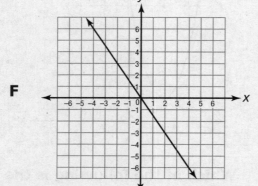

H

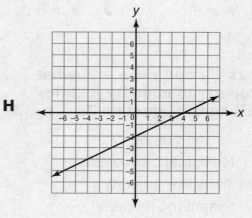

G

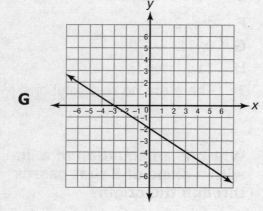

J

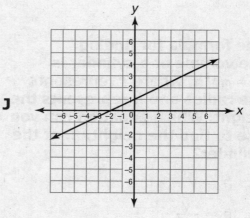

GO ON

23 Which number is a solution of the equation below?

$$x^2 - 3x - 18 = 0$$

A 0

B 2

C 3

D 6

24 Amanda sells hand-knit hats for $20 each. She must pay $100 per day to rent a booth at a crafts fair. Which equation shows her profit, *p*, in dollars, for a day in which she sold *h* hats?

F $p = h(20 - 100)$

G $p = h(100 - 20)$

H $p = 20h - 100$

J $p = 20h + 100$

25 What is the solution to the following equation?

$$\frac{1}{3}(9x - 6) = 3(x + 2) - 8$$

A 0

B 1

C All real numbers

D There is no solution.

26 Which graph *best* represents the following inequality?

$$2x + y \leq 3$$

F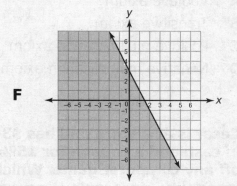

G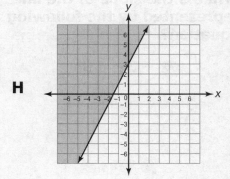

H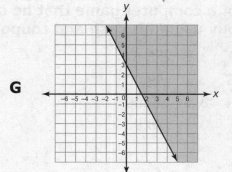

J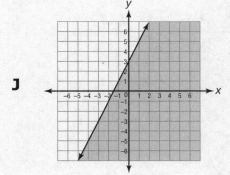

27 If $3x - 5 > 16$, what axiom of inequality justifies writing the inequality $3x > 21$?

A Additive axiom

B Transitive axiom

C Positive multiplication axiom

D Negative multiplication axiom

28 Cesar is at a store and has \$34 in cash and a coupon for 15% off any computer game. Which inequality represents the price of a computer game that he can buy using his cash and coupon?

F $x \leq 226.67$

G $x \leq 49.00$

H $x \leq 40.00$

J $x \leq 28.90$

29 What is the slope of the line represented by the following equation?

$$x + 3y = 9$$

A -3

B $-\dfrac{1}{3}$

C $\dfrac{1}{3}$

D 3

30 Which of these graphs could be used to find the solution for the following system of linear equations?

$$\begin{cases} 3x + y = 5 \\ y = {}^{-}x + 3 \end{cases}$$

F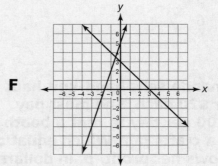

G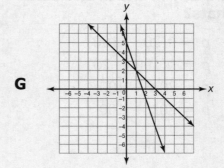

H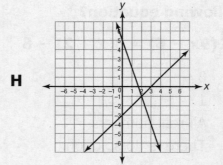

J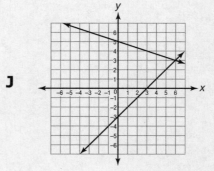

GO ON

31 Which graph *best* represents the solution to the following system of linear inequalities?

$$\begin{cases} y < \frac{1}{2}x + 2 \\ 3x + y \le 2 \end{cases}$$

A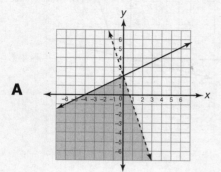

B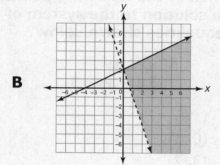

C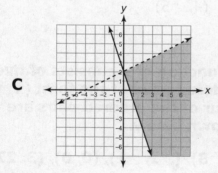

D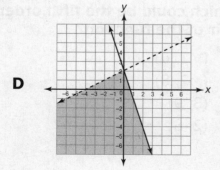

32 If $y < 3x$ and $y > -9$, what axiom of inequality justifies writing the inequality $3x > -9$?

F Additive axiom

G Transitive axiom

H Positive multiplication axiom

J Negative multiplication axiom

33 What is the solution to the following equation?

$$-4(x + 3) + 8 = 2(x + 4)$$

A -6

B -2

C 2

D 6

34 If $3m = 15$, what property of equality justifies writing $2k - 10 = k + 3m$ as $2k - 10 = k + 15$?

F Addition property

G Transitive property

H Symmetric property

J Substitution property

GO ON

35 The Smith family spent $23.50 on 3 containers of popcorn and 4 sodas at the movie theater. A container of popcorn costs $2 more than a soda. If *C* is the price of a container of popcorn and *S* is the price of a soda, which system of equations could be used to find the price of each container of popcorn and each soda?

A $\begin{cases} C + S = 2 \\ 3C + 4S = 23.5 \end{cases}$

B $\begin{cases} S = C + 2 \\ C + S = 23.5 \end{cases}$

C $\begin{cases} C = S + 2 \\ 3C + 4S = 23.5 \end{cases}$

D $\begin{cases} S = C + 2 \\ 3C + 4S = 23.5 \end{cases}$

36 The lines $3x - y = 3$ and $x = 4y$ are graphed on the coordinate grid below.

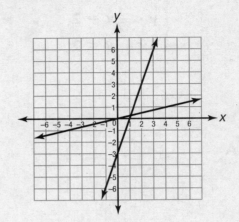

Which of the following points is a solution to the system of inequalities shown below?

$$\begin{cases} x \le 4y \\ 3x - y \ge 3 \end{cases}$$

F $(-2, -2)$

G $(0, 1)$

H $(3, 2)$

J $(4, -5)$

37 A function of *x* consists of five ordered pairs of the form (*x*, *y*). Four of the ordered pairs are shown below.

$(-2, -8), (-1, -1), (0, 0), (3, 27)$

Which could be the fifth ordered pair of the function?

A $(-1, 0)$

B $(-2, 8)$

C $(3, 9)$

D $(2, 8)$

GO ON

38 The O'Donnell and Lee families both went fishing every day in August. They each recorded the number of fish they caught each day. The box-and-whisker plots summarize the data.

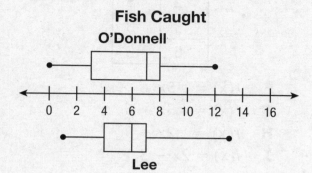

Fish Caught
O'Donnell

Lee

Which of the following is true?

F The range of fish caught per day was greater for the Lees than for the O'Donnells.

G The median number of fish caught per day was the same for both families.

H The O'Donnells caught the most fish in one day.

J The interquartile range of fish caught per day was greater for the O'Donnells than for the Lees.

39 Which of the following graphs shows a direct variation?

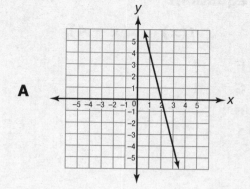

A

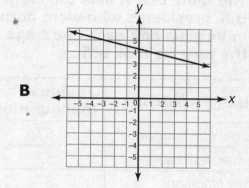

B

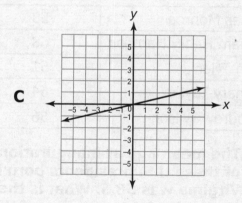

C

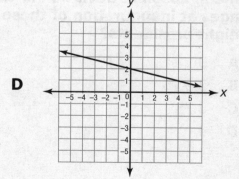

D

40 Which is a zero of the function defined by the following equation?

$$f(x) = x(x - 4)$$

F -4

G -1

H   1

J   4

41 The table below lists the eight U.S. presidents who were born in Virginia and each one's age at the time he took office.

U.S. President	Age at Inauguration
George Washington	57
Thomas Jefferson	57
James Madison	57
James Monroe	58
William Henry Harrison	68
John Tyler	51
Zachary Taylor	64
Woodrow Wilson	56

The mean age at inauguration of these U.S. presidents born in Virginia was 58.5. What is the mean absolute deviation of the ages at inauguration of these eight presidents?

A   3

B   3.5

C   3.75

D   4

42 Which function is represented by the table below?

x	f(x)
-3	15
2	5
3	3
6	-3

F $f(x) = -5x$

G $f(x) = -3x + 6$

H $f(x) = -2x + 9$

J $f(x) = 2x - 3$

43 What is the *y*-intercept of the function graphed below?

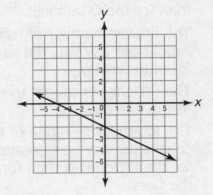

A $(0, -4)$

B $(0, -2)$

C $(0, 2)$

D $(0, 4)$

GO ON

44 This graph shows the height of an object at various times after it was propelled from a platform.

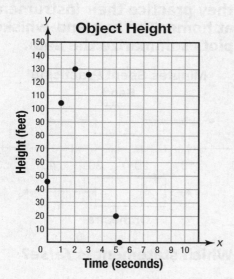

Object Height

According to a quadratic curve of best fit for these data, which is the *best* prediction for the height of the object after 4 seconds?

F 45 feet

G 62 feet

H 89 feet

J 108 feet

45 Which of the following equations is *not* a function?

A $y = {}^-6x + 2$

B $y = \frac{3}{2}x^2$

C $y = 10$

D $y^2 = 2x$

46 What is the value of $f(x) = 3x + 8$ when $x = {}^-5$?

F $^-23$ **H** 7

G $^-7$ **J** 23

47 A moving company weighs a sample of eight boxes belonging to a client. The weights are shown in the table below.

Weight (pounds)	30	34	21	26	21	35	27	30

What is the approximate standard deviation of the weights of boxes belonging to the client?

A 4.25   **C** 5.3

B 4.7   **D** 5.9

48 What are the domain and range of the function shown?

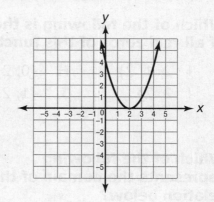

F Domain: all real numbers; Range: $y \geq 2$

G Domain: all real numbers; Range: $y \geq 0$

H Domain: $x \geq 2$; Range: $y \geq 0$

J Domain: all real numbers; Range: all real numbers

GO ON

49 The total number of hours, *h*, to plant lettuce in Bill's field varies inversely as the number of people planting the field, *n*. If *k* is the constant of variation, what equation represents that situation?

A $h = \frac{k}{n}$　　　**C** $h = n - k$

B $h = \frac{n}{k}$　　　**D** $h = kn$

50 The function $y = -\frac{1}{4}x^2 + 1$ is graphed below.

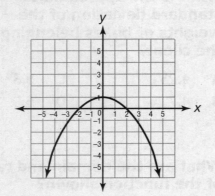

Which of the following is the set of all real zeros of this function?

F {$^-2$, 1, 2}　　**H** {0, 2}

G {$^-2$, 2}　　　**J** {1, 2}

51 Which of the following represents the domain of the relation below?

{($^-4$, 2), ($^-2$, 1), (0, 0), (2, $^-1$)}

A {$^-4$, $^-2$, 0, 2}

B {$^-2$, 0, 1, 2}

C {$^-1$, 0, 1, 2}

D {$^-4$, $^-2$, $^-1$, 0, 1, 2}

52 Mrs. Chen surveyed the members of the school band and the school orchestra to find out how many minutes per day they practice their instruments at home. The box-and-whisker plots summarize the data.

Minutes Spent Practicing

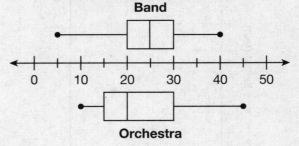

Which statement is *false*?

F The difference in the maximum number of minutes per day of practice for band and orchestra members is 5.

G The range of practice times is the same for orchestra members as for band members.

H The median number of minutes per day of practice is greater for the band than for the orchestra.

J The interquartile range of practice times is the same for orchestra members as for band members.

53 The table shows the number of minutes Ashwin played in each basketball game over the season and how many points he scored in each game.

Minutes Played (m)	15	20	25	30	35	40	50	60
Points Scored (p)	0	3	6	6	10	11	15	20

Which equation *most* closely represents a line of best fit for the data?

A $p = {}^-0.4m + 6$

B $p = 0.4m - 6$

C $p = {}^-6m + 0.4$

D $p = 6m - 0.4$

54 Alethea is taking a bus to visit her aunt. The function $f(x) = 375 - 55x$ gives the distance she has left to travel after riding for x hours on the bus. What is $f(4)$, the distance she has left to travel after riding for 4 hours on the bus?

F 155 miles

G 165 miles

H 179 miles

J 220 miles

55 This table shows the number of wins per season for the University of Virginia Cavaliers for six consecutive seasons.

Season	Number of Games Won
2005/06	7
2006/07	5
2007/08	9
2008/09	5
2009/10	3
2010/11	4

The standard deviation for the data is 2. Which z-score represents 4, the number of games won in 2010/11?

A $^-1.5$

B $^-0.75$

C 0.75

D 1.5

56 Which of the following lists all x-intercepts of the function defined by the following equation?

$$f(x) = x^2 + 6x - 16$$

F (8, 0) and ($^-2$, 0)

G (4, 0) and ($^-4$, 0)

H (2, 0) and ($^-8$, 0)

J ($^-16$, 0)

GO ON

57 Which function is represented by the graph below?

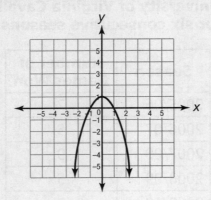

A $\quad y = x^2 - 1$

B $\quad y = x^2 + 1$

C $\quad y = -x^2 - 1$

D $\quad y = -x^2 + 1$

58 If $f(x) = 5\sqrt{16 - x}$ what is $f(7)$?

F $\quad -15$

G $\quad 8$

H $\quad 13$

J $\quad 15$

59 Which table shows a relation that is a function?

A

x	−3	0	3	4
$f(x)$	8	−1	8	15

B

x	−4	−1	2	2
$f(x)$	2	5	8	11

C

x	4	1	4	9
$f(x)$	−3	2	3	4

D

x	6	6	6	6
$f(x)$	5	4	3	2

60 This table shows the number of hours, h, to drive 240 miles at various speeds, s.

Speed (miles per hour), s	30	40	50	60
Time (hours), h	8	6	4.8	4

Which best describes the relationship between s and h in this table?

F $\quad$ Linear function

G $\quad$ Quadratic function

H $\quad$ Indirect variation

J $\quad$ Direct variation

STOP

**Virginia End-of-Course Coach
Algebra I**

Practice Test 2

Name: _____

Directions

Read each question and choose the best answer. For this test you may assume that the value of the denominator is not zero.

SAMPLE

The relationship shown in the table is a direct variation.

x	y
−2	8
−1	4
0	0
1	−4

Which equation *best* represents this relationship?

A $y = -\frac{1}{4}x$

B $y = x + 10$

C $y = -2x + 4$

D $y = -4x$

GO ON

Practice Test 2

1 Which of the following is equivalent to $\dfrac{30x^6y}{5x^3y^2}$?

A $\dfrac{6x^2}{y}$

B $\dfrac{6x^2}{y^3}$

C $\dfrac{6x^3}{y}$

D $\dfrac{6x^3}{y^3}$

2 What is $\sqrt{108}$ expressed in simplest radical form?

F $8\sqrt{2}$

G $6\sqrt{3}$

H $3\sqrt{12}$

J $2\sqrt{27}$

3 Which labeled point on the number line is closest to the cube root of 45?

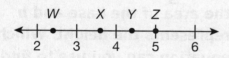

A W

B X

C Y

D Z

4 Which expression is equivalent to $(6x^2 + 11x + 4) \div (3x + 4)$?

F $x + 1$

G $2x + 1$

H $2x + 3$

J $2x + 7$

5 What is the value of the expression $\sqrt{3xy - 32}$ when $x = 9$ and $y = 3$?

A -26

C 2

B -23

D 7

6 $\boxed{} = x^2$ $\boxed{} = x$ $\boxed{} = 1$

Based on the models for x^2, x, and 1, which product is represented by the diagram?

F $(2x + 2)(x + 4)$

G $(2x + 2)(2x + 2)$

H $(2x + 2)(2x^2 + 2x)$

J $(2x^2 + 2x)(2x^2 + 2x)$

7 Which polynomial is equivalent to the following expression?

$(5x^2 - x + 8) - (3x^2 - 2x + 4)$

A $2x^2 + x + 12$

B $2x^2 - 3x + 4$

C $2x^2 + x + 4$

D $2x^2 - x + 4$

8 A factored form of $x^2 - 9x + 20$ is —

F $(x + 4)(x + 5)$

G $(x + 2)(x - 10)$

H $(x - 4)(x - 5)$

J $(x - 2)(x - 10)$

Practice Test 2

9 The height of a certain cylinder is five more than four times its diameter. If the diameter of the cylinder is 6 units, what is its height?

A 11
B 15
C 19
D 29

10 Which is equivalent to the following expression?

$$(2xy^3)(4x^2y^2)$$

F $6x^2y^6$
G $6x^3y^5$
H $8x^2y^6$
J $8x^3y^5$

11 What is $\sqrt{4x^3y^6}$ expressed in *simplest* radical form?

A $2xy^4$
B $2xy^3\sqrt{x}$
C $2xy^4\sqrt{x}$
D $2x^2y^4\sqrt{x}$

12 Which of the following equals $6x^2 - 5x - 6$ when factored completely?

F $(3x + 2)(2x - 3)$
G $(6x + 1)(x - 6)$
H $(3x - 1)(2x - 6)$
J $(3x - 3)(2x - 2)$

13 Jeremy is saving up money to buy a laptop computer. So far, he has saved $210. If he saves $40 per week, how much will he have saved *w* weeks from now?

A $210 + 40w$
B $210 + 40 + w$
C $210 - 40w$
D $w(210 + 40)$

14 A factored form of $16x^2 - 81$ is –

F $16(x^2 - 5)$
G $(8x + 9)(8x - 9)$
H $(4x + 9)(4x - 9)$
J $(4x + 9)(2x + 3)(2x - 3)$

15 The formula for finding the volume of a rectangular pyramid is $V = \frac{1}{3}Bh$, where *B* represents the area of the base and *h* represents the height. Which equation can you use to find the area of the base, *B*, of the rectangular prism?

A $B = \frac{3V}{h}$ C $B = \frac{Vh}{3}$

B $B = \frac{V}{3h}$ D $B = \frac{h}{3V}$

16 What is the solution to the following equation?

$$4(-2x + 3) = 10x - 15$$

F $-\frac{1}{6}$ H 1

G 0 J $\frac{3}{2}$

17 Which graph *best* represents the following inequality?

$$y \geq -\frac{1}{2}x - 2$$

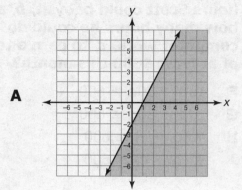

A

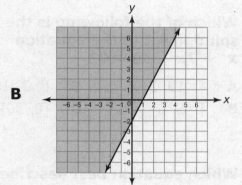

B

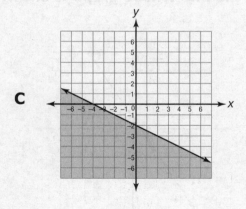

C

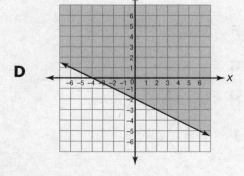

D

18 Jordan earns $380 per week as well as a commission of 3% of her sales. If she wants to earn at least $500 total in one week, which inequality represents the amount, in dollars, she must sell that week?

F $x \geq 360$

G $x \geq 400$

H $x \geq 3,600$

J $x \geq 4,000$

19 Which is an equation of a line with a slope of -2 that passes through the point (-4, 10)?

A $y = -3x - 2$

B $y = -2x + 2$

C $y = -2x + 14$

D $y = -2x + 18$

20 Which *best* describes the slope of the line whose graph is shown?

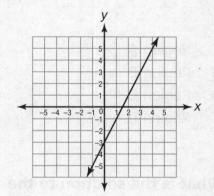

A -3

B -2

C 2

D 3

GO ON

21 If $-2x > 4$, what axiom of inequality justifies writing the inequality $x < -2$?

    A Additive axiom

    B Transitive axiom

    C Positive multiplication axiom

    D Negative multiplication axiom

22 Which region of the graph shown below represents the solution to the following system of linear inequalities?

$$\begin{cases} y < 2x - 4 \\ x - 3y < 3 \end{cases}$$

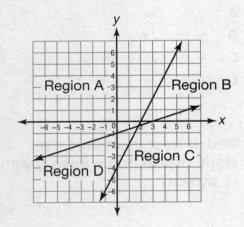

    F Region A

    G Region B

    H Region C

    J Region D

23 What is the solution to the following equation?

$$2(x - 7) + 3 = -3(x - 3)$$

    A -20 **C** $\dfrac{2}{5}$

    B -2 **D** 4

24 Scott earns $10 per hour for babysitting and $30 per hour for computer repair work. Which inequality represents how many hours Scott could babysit, *b*, and how many hours he could do computer work, *c*, to earn a total of at least $600 this month?

    F $10b + 30c \geq 600$

    G $10b + 30c \leq 600$

    H $40(b + c) \geq 600$

    J $40(b + c) \leq 600$

25 Which of the following is the solution set to the equation $x^2 + 7x - 30 = 0$?

    A $\{-10, 3\}$ **C** $\{-3, 10\}$

    B $\{-5, 6\}$ **D** $\{0, 30\}$

26 Which equation *best* describes the line whose graph is shown?

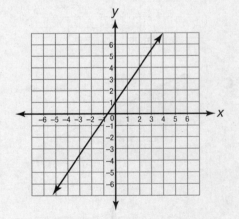

    F $y = x + \dfrac{2}{3}$

    G $y = x + \dfrac{3}{2}$

    H $y = \dfrac{2}{3}x + 1$

    J $y = \dfrac{3}{2}x + 1$

Practice Test 2

27 The formula for finding the area of a triangle is $A = \frac{1}{2}bh$, where b represents the length of the base and h represents the height. Which equation gives the height, h, of a triangle in terms of its area and base length?

A $h = A - \frac{1}{2}b$

C $h = \frac{2A}{b}$

B $h = 2Ab$

D $h = \frac{2b}{A}$

28 Which is the solution for the system of linear equations whose graphs are shown below?

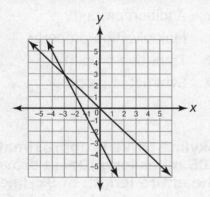

F $(-3, -3)$ **H** $(-3, 3)$

G $(-3, 0)$ **J** $(0, 0)$

29 When shopping for school supplies for her children, Mrs. McCormick bought 3 packs of pens and 4 binders for a total cost of $16.75. Mr. Mathai bought 2 of the same packs of pens and 5 of the same binders for a total cost of $17.00. How much does one binder cost?

A $2.25   **C** $3.25

B $2.50   **D** $4.00

30 If $\frac{2}{3}n = 6$, what property of equality justifies writing the equation $n = 9$?

F Addition property

G Multiplication property

H Transitive property

J Symmetric property

31 What is the slope of the line represented by the following equation?

$$y = 3x + 6$$

A $^-2$

B $\frac{1}{3}$

C 3

D 6

32 The function $y = x^2 + 4x - 5$ is graphed below.

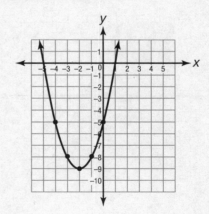

Which of the following is the solution set to the equation $x^2 + 4x - 5 = 0$?

F $\{-5, 1\}$

G $\{-2, -9\}$

H $\{-1, 5\}$

J $\{0, -5\}$

GO ON

33 Which graph *best* represents the following inequality?

$$y \geq {}^{-}2x + 3$$

A

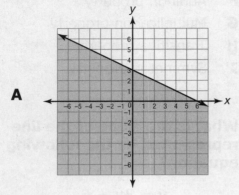

B

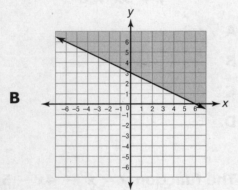

C

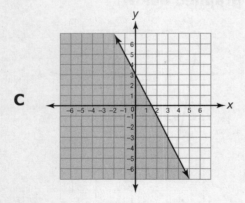

D

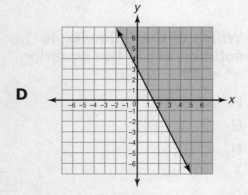

34 What is the solution of the system of linear equations below?

$$\begin{cases} 3x - 2y = {}^{-}6 \\ 2x + 2 = y \end{cases}$$

F $({}^{-}2, {}^{-}2)$

G $(2, 6)$

H $(4, 10)$

J $(8, 18)$

35 If ${}^{-}2x + 7 = 2x + 9$, what property of equality justifies writing the equation $7 = 4x + 9$?

A Addition property

B Multiplication property

C Transitive property

D Symmetric property

36 Skyline Drive is approximately 105 miles long. David drove the entire length of Skyline Drive at a steady speed of 35 miles per hour. He also took a one-hour lunch break at an overlook along the way. How much time did David spend, in all, on Skyline Drive?

F 2 hours

G 3 hours

H 4 hours

J 5 hours

GO ON

Practice Test 2

37 What is the *y*-intercept of the function defined by the following equation?

$$f(x) = x^2 - 6x + 9$$

A (0, −6)

B (0, −3)

C (0, 3)

D (0, 9)

38 The function $f(x) = 560 + 50x$ gives the amount, in dollars, in Omar's savings account after he has saved for *x* months. What is $f(9)$, the amount in his savings account after Omar saved for 9 months?

F $619

G $910

H $1,010

J $1,069

39 Which of the following represents the range of the relation shown below?

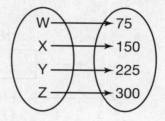

A {W, X, Y, Z}

B {W, X, 75, 150}

C {75, 150, 225, 300}

D {W, 75, X, 150, Y, 225, Z, 300}

40 The relationship shown in the table is an inverse variation.

x	y
2	18
3	12
4	9
6	6

Which equation *best* represents this relationship?

F $y = \dfrac{36}{x}$

G $y = 9x$

H $y = 6x - 6$

J $y = 24 - 3x$

GO ON

Practice Test 2

41 The ninth-grade and tenth-grade students in Ms. Rossman's classes recorded the number of days they went to the beach last summer. The box-and-whisker plots summarize the data.

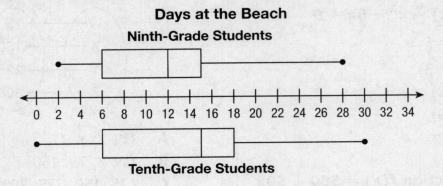

Days at the Beach

Ninth-Grade Students

Tenth-Grade Students

Which statement is *false*?

A The least number of days at the beach was the same for ninth-grade students as for tenth-grade students.

B The student who spent the greatest number of days at the beach was in tenth grade.

C The median number of days at the beach for tenth-grade students was 3 more than the median for ninth-grade students.

D The interquartile range of days at the beach was greater for tenth-grade students than for ninth-grade students.

42 Which table represents the function $f(x) = 3x - 12$?

F

x	0	2	4	7
f(x)	−12	−6	0	9

G

x	1	3	6	8
f(x)	−9	−3	0	12

H

x	2	4	5	6
f(x)	−6	0	15	6

J

x	0	1	2	6
f(x)	−12	−9	−6	3

43 The best-run scores for the top five finishers in the finals for the men's halfpipe snowboarding competition of the 2010 Winter Olympics are shown below.

48.4, 45.0, 42.8, 42.4, 39.4

Which value represents the approximate standard deviation for these five scores?

A 2.5

B 3.0

C 4.4

D 8.9

44 What is the range of the function described by the equation below?

$$f(x) = x^2 - 8x + 12$$

F $f(x) \leq 12$

G $f(x) \geq 0$

H $f(x) \geq -4$

J $\{f(x): f(x) \in \mathbb{R}\}$

45 Mrs. Avila noticed a relationship between the time at which she left for work in the morning and the number of minutes she took to get to work. Mrs. Avila recorded her data in the scatterplot below.

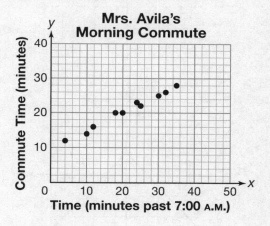

Mrs. Avila's Morning Commute

According to a line of best fit for this data, which is the *best* prediction of how long Mrs. Avila will take to get to work if she leaves at 8:00 A.M.?

A 30 minutes

B 40 minutes

C 50 minutes

D 60 minutes

GO ON

46 Which graph apparently represents a function of *x*?

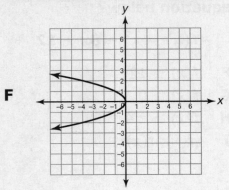

F

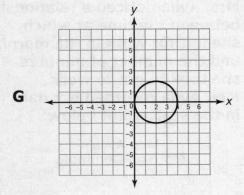

G

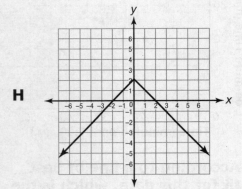

H

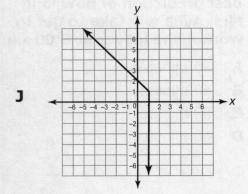

J

47 The table gives the cost for different numbers of toothbrushes. The cost, *C*, varies directly as the number of toothbrushes, *n*.

Number of Toothbrushes (*n*)	Cost (*C*)
2	$5.70
4	$11.40
6	$17.10
8	$22.80

Which equation represents the relationship shown in the table?

A $C = 2.85 + n$

B $C = \dfrac{2.85}{n}$

C $C = 2.85n$

D $C = 5.70n$

48 What is the domain of the function shown?

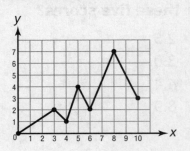

F $0 \leq x \leq 7$

G $0 \leq x \leq 10$

H $1 \leq x \leq 7$

J $1 \leq x \leq 10$

GO ON

49 If $f(x) = x^2 + 3x + 5$, what is the value of $f(x)$ when $x = -4$?

A -23
B 9
C 20
D 33

50 The line plot shows the surface areas, in square feet, of the nine desks sold by Matt's Furniture Store.

Desk Areas

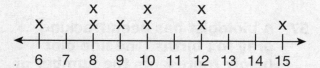

6 7 8 9 10 11 12 13 14 15

What is the mean absolute deviation of desk surface areas at Matt's Furniture Store?

F 2 square feet
G 2.5 square feet
H 6.4 square feet
J 10 square feet

51 What is the x-intercept of the function defined by the following equation?

$$f(x) = -4x + 16$$

A $(-16, 0)$
B $(-4, 0)$
C $(4, 0)$
D $(16, 0)$

52 Which is a zero of the function defined by the following equation?

$$f(x) = (x - 1)(x + 3)$$

F -3
G 0
H 2
J 3

53 Nadiya is withdrawing money at a bank. The teller gave her several options of bill denominations and quantities, as shown in the table below. The number of bills, n, varies inversely with the denomination, d, in dollars per bill.

Denomination (dollars per bill), d	Number of Bills, n
10	30
20	15
50	6
100	3

Which equation represents the relationship shown in the table?

A $n = 3d$

B $n = 300d$

C $n = 300 - d$

D $n = \dfrac{300}{d}$

GO ON

54 An ice cream store recorded its weekly number of customers for 12 weeks, starting at Memorial Day. This table shows the data.

Weeks After Memorial Day (w)	1	2	3	4	5	6	7	8	9	10	11	12
Number of Customers (c)	173	242	300	338	376	400	415	420	416	400	373	340

Which equation *most* closely represents a curve of best fit for the data?

F $c = -5w^2 + 80w + 100$

G $c = -5w^2 + 80w - 100$

H $c = 5w^2 - 80w + 100$

J $c = 5w^2 + 80w - 100$

---

55 Which relation is *not* a function?

A $\{(-4, 4), (-3, 3), (0, 0), (4, 4)\}$

B $\{(2, 9), (4, 7), (6, 5), (8, 5)\}$

C $\{(3, 0), (0, 2), (5, 9), (3, 7)\}$

D $\{(-2, 1), (0, 1), (1, -2), (3, 4)\}$

56 Which is a zero of the function defined by the following equation?

$$f(x) = 2x^2 - 8x$$

F -4

G $-\dfrac{1}{2}$

H $\dfrac{1}{2}$

J 4

57 A biologist has been tracking gray fox births. The line plot below represents the number of kits born in each of eight litters in a given fox population.

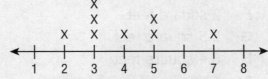

Gray Fox Litters

Number of Kits per Litter

The standard deviation for this data set is 1.5. What is the z-score associated with the litter of 7 kits in this gray fox population?

A   1.5

B   2

C   3

D   4.5

GO ON